FOREWORD

The songs contained in this book are a compilation of Integrity Music's 200 best-selling Praise and Worship songs. They're arranged in four-part harmony (SATB) and can be easily performed by your choir, worship team, congregation or even your family. The four-part harmony also works well as a basis for piano and organ accompaniment. Cued notes have been added where necessary to help establish the "feel" of the song. Guitar chords are also provided.

Musicians should be encouraged to embellish these arrangments by improvising with the chord symbols. When there is a note under a slash (e.g., F/G), the note above the slash is the chord to be played by the upper register instruments (guitar, right hand of the piano, etc.). The note below the slash is to be played by the lower register instruments (bass guitar, organ pedals, left hand of the piano, etc.). For songs that flow smoothly with each other, a medley reference is listed on each appropriate page.

Top 200 has many helpful features:

> Index "A" lists songs by the first line of lyrics in case you are unsure of the title.

> Index "B" lists the songs according to their Scriptural references. If you are searching for a song featuring a specific Scripture, you will find it listed in biblical order.

> Index "C" lists the songs by topic, such as joy, thanksgiving, victory, etc. If you know the theme of your pastor's message, you can prepare the hearts of the people by focusing your worship on the same topic.

> Index "D" lists all songs by key and tempo. Praise and worship times will flow more smoothly if you select songs that are closely related in key and tempo. Create medleys of songs rather than stopping after each song. Choose songs that are related thematically.

> Index "E" provides 15 worship packages of songs from this book. Each package is approximately 20 minutes in length and thematic in nature wherever possible. Key suggestions are also provided for each song.

We trust that this book will become a frequently used favorite. Our Praise Worship words only book makes a great companion to this collection.

D1261896

Printing

11 12 13 14 15 16 17 18 19 20

TABLE of CONTENTS

1 A Shield About Me

Words and Music by
DONN THOMAS and CHARLES WILLIAMS

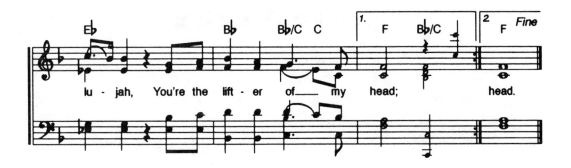

Medley options: Hear My Cry; In the Presence.

2 Above All Else

Words and Music by
KIRK and DEBY DEARMAN

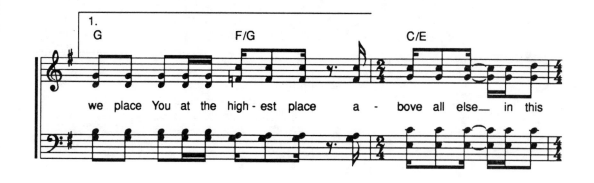

we place You at the high - est place a - bove all else___ in this

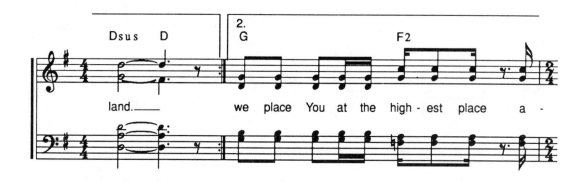

land.___ we place You at the high - est place a -

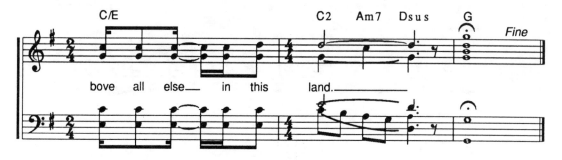

bove all else___ in this land.___

Medley options: We Declare That the Kingdom of God Is Here; Mighty Warrior.

Ah, Lord God

3

Words and Music by
KAY CHANCE

Medley options: Let the Redeemed; In Him We Live.

All Consuming Fire

4

Words and Music by
RANDY WRIGHT

Medley options: More Love, More Power; Awesome God.

Worship the Lord in holy attire; tremble before Him, all the earth. Psalm 96:9

All Creation Worships You   5

Words and Music by
KIRK DEARMAN and JIM MILLS

Medley options: On Bended Knee; Praise Him.

6 All Hail King Jesus

Words and Music by
DAVE MOODY

Medley options: Lift Up Your Heads; Thou Art Worthy, Great Jehovah.

All of us like sheep have gone astray. Isaiah 53:6

All We Like Sheep

7

Words and Music by
DON MOEN

Medley options: There Is None Holy as the Lord; Purify My Heart.

8

Great and marvelous are Your works, Lord God Almighty!
Just and true are your ways, O King of the saints! Revelation 15:3

Almighty

Words and Music by
WAYNE WATSON

Medley options: God Is the Strength of My Heart.

For it is by grace you have been saved. Ephesians 2:8

Amazing Grace

9

Traditional American Melody

Words by
JOHN NEWTON

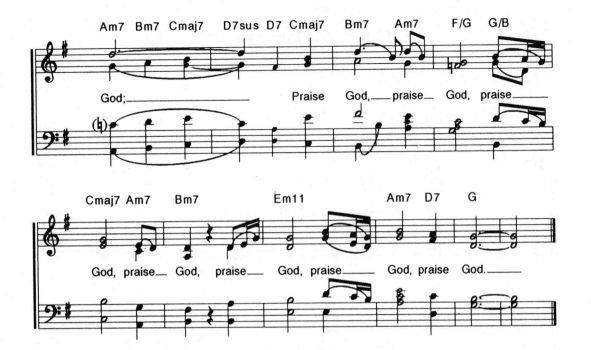

Medley options: Thou Art Worthy; Worthy the Lamb That Was Slain.

But God demonstrated His own love toward us,
in that while we were yet sinners, Christ died for us. Romans 5:8

Amazing Love

Words and Music by
GRAHAM KENDRICK

My Lord,_____ what love is this_____ that
And so_____ they watched Him die,_____ de-
And now_____ this love of Christ_____ shall

pays_____ so dear - ly;_____ That I,_____ the
spised,_____ re - ject - ed;_____ But O_____ the
flow_____ like riv - ers;_____ Come wash_____ your

guilt - y one_____ may go free._____
blood He shed_____ flowed for me._____ A-
guilt a - way,_____ live a - gain._____

CHORUS

maz - ing love,_____ O what sac - ri - fice,_____ The Son of God,_____

Medley options: More Than Anything; No Other Name.

11 Ancient of Days

Words and Music by
GARY SADLER and JAMIE HARVILL

CHORUS

Ev-'ry tongue___ in heav-en and earth___ shall de-clare___ Your glo-ry,

ev-'ry knee___ shall bow at Your throne___ in wor-ship;

You will be___ ex-alt-ed, O God,___ and Your

king-dom___ shall not pass a-way,___ O An-cient of Days.___

Your

BRIDGE

king - dom____ shall reign o - ver all the earth,

sing un - to____ the An - cient____ of____ Days; For

none can____ com - pare to____ Your match - less worth,

sing un - to____ the An - cient____ of____ Days.

Medley options: Clap, Clap Your Hands; We Declare That the Kingdom of God Is Here.

Let me inherit a double portion of your spirit. 2 Kings 2:9

Anointing Fall on Me

12

Words and Music by
DONN THOMAS

Medley options: All Consuming Fire; My Soul Follows Hard After Thee.

Arise, go down against the camp, for I have given it into your hands. Judges 7:9

Arise and Sing

13

Words and Music by
MEL RAY

Medley options: Hosanna; Chosen Generation.

14 # Arise, Shine

Words and Music by
STEVEN URSPRINGER and JAY ROBINSON

Medley options: Like A Shepherd.

Praise Him with timbrel and dancing. Psalm 150:4

15 As David Did

Words and Music by
MARTIN J. NYSTROM

Medley options: Blow the Trumpet in Zion; Make a Joyful Noise.

Come and see the works of God, who is
awesome in His deeds toward the sons of men. Psalm 66:5

Awesome God

Words and Music by
RICH MULLINS

Medley options: All Consuming Fire; More Love, More Power.

Be strong and courageous! ...for the Lord your God is with you. Joshua 1:9

Be Bold, Be Strong

17

Words and Music by
MORRIS CHAPMAN

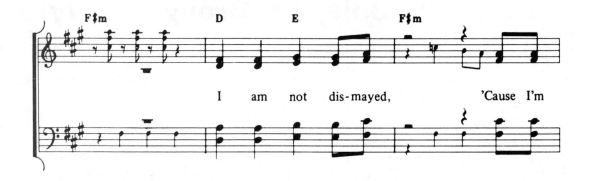

I am not dis-mayed, 'Cause I'm

walk - in' in faith and vic - to-ry. Come on and

walk in faith and vic - to-ry, For the Lord,___ your

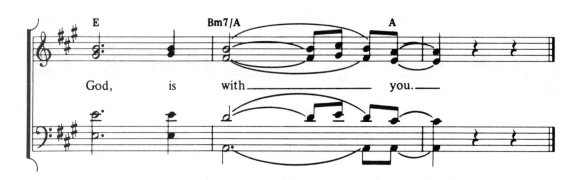

God, is with_____ you.___

Medley options: Blessed Be the Rock; The Lord Is Come.

Be exalted above the heavens, O God; let Thy glory be above all the earth. Psalm 57:11

Be Exalted, O God

18

Words and Music by
BRENT CHAMBERS

Medley options: Crown Him; All Hail King Jesus.

19   **Be Glorified**

Words and Music by
BILLY FUNK

1. Be glo - ri - fied,_____ be glo - ri - fied;_____
2. Wor - ship the Lord,_____ wor - ship the Lord;_____

Be glo - ri - fied,_____ be glo - ri - fied._____
Wor - ship the Lord,_____ wor - ship the Lord._____

Be glo - ri - fied_____ in the heav - ens,
Wor - ship the Lord_____ in the heav - ens,

be glo - ri - fied_____ in the earth;_____
wor - ship the Lord_____ in the earth;_____

Medley options: In the Presence; I Stand in Awe.

Be Magnified

Words a
LYNN

Lord, be mag - ni - fied._____

Medley options: In the Presence; I Stand in Awe.

Be strong and of good courage...fear not, nor be dismayed:
for the Lord God...will be with thee. 1 Chronicles 28:20

Strong and Take Courage

Words and Music by
BASIL CHIASSON

Lyrics underlaid in the music:

Be strong___ and take cour - age, do not fear or___ be___ dis - mayed;___ For the Lord will go be- fore you, and His light will show___ the way. So, be strong___ and take cour - age,___ do not

Medley options: More Than Conquerors; God Will Make a Way.

Blessed Be the Lo...
God Almighty

Wor...

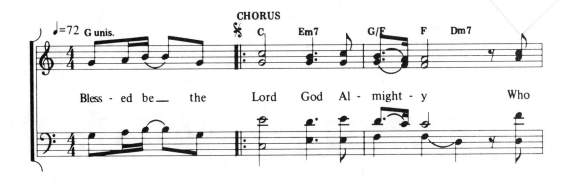

Bless-ed be— the Lord God Al-might-y Who

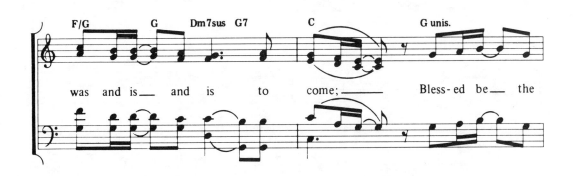

was and is— and is to come;—— Bless-ed be— the

Lord God Al-might-y Who reigns for-ev-er-more._

Medley options: Oh the Glory of Your Presence; When I Look Into Your Holiness.

Let the name of God be blessed forever and ever. Daniel 2:20

Blessed Be the Name
of the Lord

Words and Music by
DON MOEN

Medley options: Worthy, You Are Worthy; I Am the God That Healeth Thee; Holy Ground (Davis).

24 **Blessed Be the Rock**

Words and Music by
DANIEL GARDNER

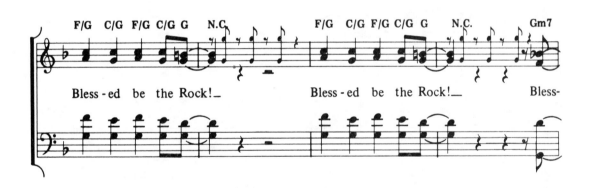

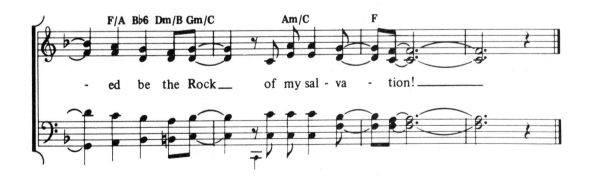

Medley options: Be Bold, Be Strong; You Are Crowned With Many Crowns.

Arise, bless the Lord your God forever and ever! O, may Thy glorious name be blessed and exalted above all blessing and praise! Thou alone art the Lord. Nehemiah 9:5,6

Blessed Be Your Glorious Name

25

Words and Music by
RIC MARCHI

Medley options: Blessed Be the Name of the Lord; More Precious Than Silver;
I Worship You, Almighty God.

Blow a trumpet in Zion, and sound an alarm on My holy mountain! Joel 2:1

26 Blow the Trumpet in Zion

Words and Music by
CRAIG TERNDRUP

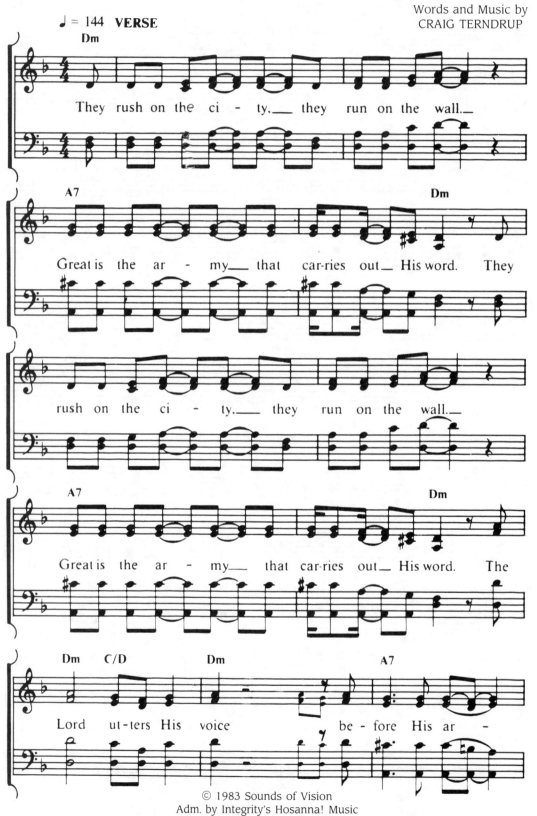

They rush on the ci - ty,__ they run on the wall.__

Great is the ar - my__ that car-ries out__ His word. They

rush on the ci - ty,__ they run on the wall.__

Great is the ar - my__ that car-ries out__ His word. The

Lord ut-ters His voice be - fore His ar -

Medley options: The Lord Is Building Jerusalem.

the Lord always; again I say, rejoice! Philippians 4:4

Celebrate Jesus

Words and Music by
GARY OLIVER

Medley options: Come and Worship; The Lord Is Come.

Create in me a clean heart, O God, and renew a steadfast spirit within me. Psalm 51:10
We are the clay, and Thou our potter, and all of us are the work of Thy hand. Isaiah 64:8

28 Change My Heart, Oh God

Words and Music by
EDDIE ESPINOSA

Medley options: Hear My Cry; When I Look Into Your Holiness.

But you are a chosen race, a royal priesthood, a holy nation. 1 Peter 2:9

Chosen Generation

Words and Music by
JEANNIE CLATTENBURG and RICK POWELL

For you are a cho-sen gen-er-a-tion, a roy-al priest-hood, a ho-ly na-tion, a pe-cu-liar peo-ple, that you should show forth the prais-es of Him Who has called you out of

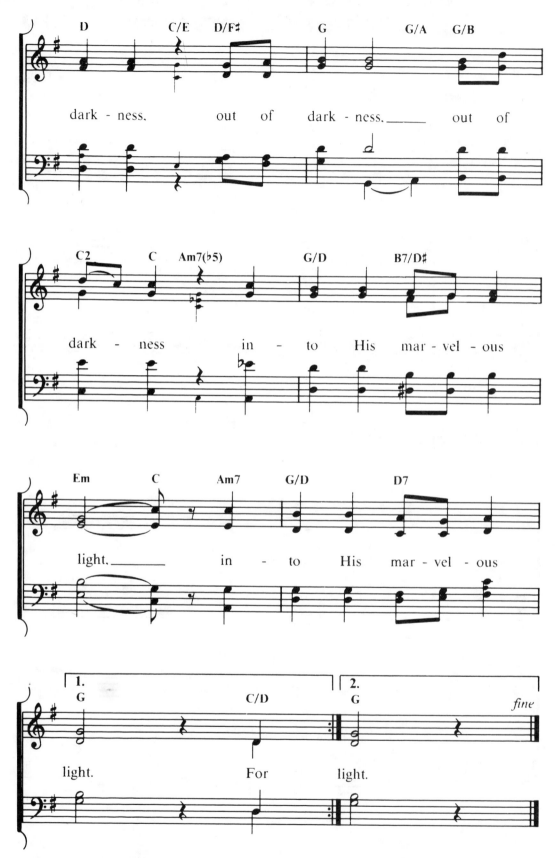

Medley options: God Is My Refuge; What a Mighty God We Serve.

O clap your hands, all peoples. Psalm 47:1

Clap, Clap Your Hands
30

Words and Music by
JENNIFER RANDOLPH

VERSE

Medley options: Lord of All; Mourning Into Dancing.

31 Clap Your Hands

Words and Music by
CHARLIE LeBLANC

VERSE

Medley options: Lord of All; Lift Him Up.

32 Come and Worship

Words and Music by
DON MOEN

1. There's a call,— it's com-ing from the moun-tain to one and all;— There's a call,— a call to ev-'ry tribe and na-tion,— wor-ship Him,— the Lamb Who sits up-on— the throne.— Come and

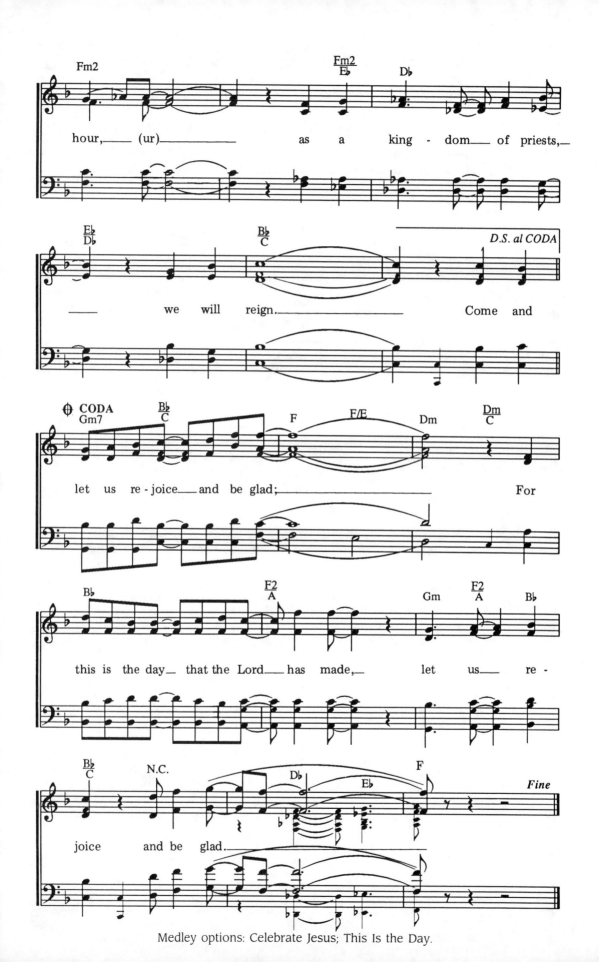

Medley options: Celebrate Jesus; This Is the Day.

Let us come before His presence with thanksgiving. Psalm 95:3

Come Into His Presence

Words and Music by
LYNN BAIRD

Medley options: Thou Shalt Love the Lord; I Will Sing of the Mercies of the Lord.

34 Come Into the Holy of Holies

Words and Music by
JOHN SELLERS

Medley options: He Is Lovely; Oh, the Glory of Your Presence.

35 Come Into
the King's Chambers

Words and Music by
DANIEL GARDNER

O come in-to the King's cham-bers and wor-ship be-fore His___ throne.___ O come in-to the King's cham-bers, and His glo-ry shall be___ shown.___ O

Medley options: More Precious Than Silver; Holy Ground.

36 Create in Me a Clean Heart

Author Unknown

Medley options: O Lord, You're Beautiful; Only Jesus.

The kingdom of the world has become the kingdom of our Lord and of His Christ, and He will reign for ever and ever. Revelation 11:15

Crown Him

Words and Music by
SHARON DAMAZIO

He shall reign, He shall reign for - ev - er - more.

Medley options: Lift Up Your Heads; Be Exalted, O God; All Hail King Jesus.

38 Exalt the Lord

Words and Music by
RICK RIDINGS

Medley options: Come Into the King's Chambers; Worthy, You Are Worthy.

Exalt the Lord Our God 39

Words and Music by
DANIEL GARDNER

Medley options: More Precious Than Silver; Who Is Like Unto Thee;
Blessed Be Your Glorious Name.

But Thou, O Lord, art on high forever. Psalm 92:8

Exalted

Words and Music by
BETTY NICHOLSON

Medley options: Thou Art Worthy, Great Jehovah; I Worship You, Almighty God.

41 Extol the Name

Words and Music by
CHARLES MATHEWS

Medley options: All Hail King Jesus; Only Jesus.

He will be the sure foundation for your times,
a rich store of salvation and wisdom and knowledge. Isaiah 33:6

42 Firm Foundation

Words and Music by
NANCY GORDON and JAMIE HARVILL

Medley options: Clap, Clap Your Hands; Mourning Into Dancing.

And they will be as mighty men. . .for the Lord will be with them. Zechariah 10:5

43 For the Lord Is Marching On

Words and Music by
BONNIE LOW

CHORUS

Cap-tain of the host is Je-sus. We're fol-low-ing in His foot-steps. No foe can stand a - gainst us in the fray. For the

2. We are

Medley options: Let God Arise; Victory Song (Through Our God).

*. . .with psalms and hymns and spiritual songs,
singing with thankfulness in your hearts to God. Colossians 3:16*

Forever Grateful

Words and Music by
MARK ALTROGGE

Medley options: Great Is the Lord; I Sing Praises; Our Heart.

45

From the rising of the sun to its setting, the name of the Lord is to be praised. Psalm 113:3

From the Rising of the Sun

Words and Music by
PAUL DEMING

Medley options: O, Clap Your Hands.

Be ye thankful. Colossians 3:15

46 Give Thanks

Words and Music by
HENRY SMITH

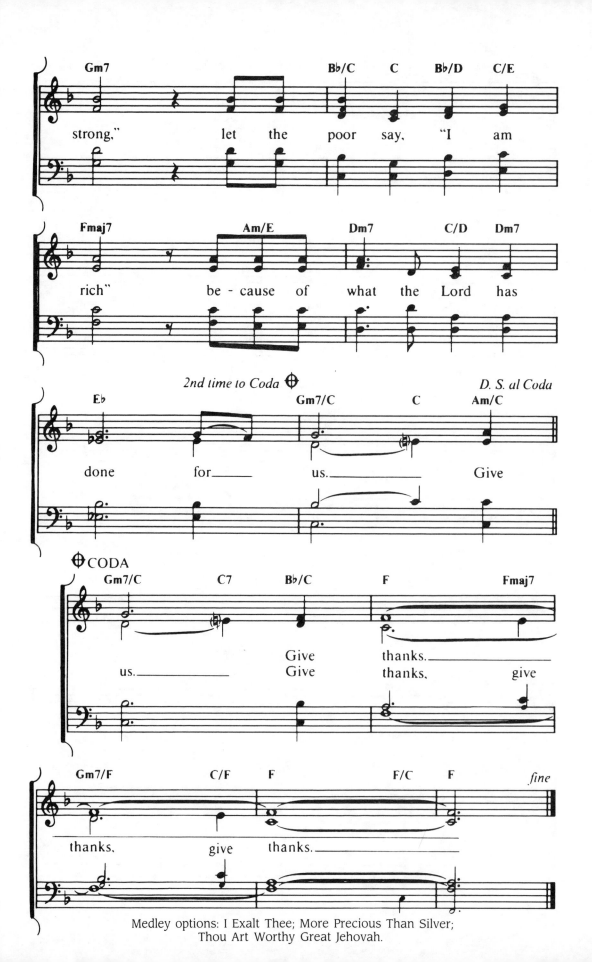

Medley options: I Exalt Thee; More Precious Than Silver;
Thou Art Worthy Great Jehovah.

Let them give glory to the Lord and proclaim His praise in the islands. Isaiah 42:12

Glory, Glory, Lord

47

Words and Music by
BOB FITTS

CHORUS

* Hawaiian
** Samoan

Medley options: The Battle Belongs to the Lord; You Have Called Us.

48

*Worthy is the Lamb that was slain to receive power and riches
and wisdom and might and honor and glory and blessing. Revelation 5:12*

Glory to the Lamb

Words and Music by
LARRY DEMPSEY

CHORUS

glo - ri - ous and wor - thy to be praised, the Lamb up - on the throne; and un - to Him we lift our voice in praise, the Lamb up - on the throne.

Medley options: Think About His Love; To Him Who Sits on the Throne.

...look on the fields, that they are white for harvest. John 4:35

Go Forth

49

Words and Music by
BOB MASON

Go forth, go forth in - to the rip-ened fields for they are white un - to har - vest. The time, the time of reap-ing is at hand for souls of men to be gath-ered in.

What was sown in tears shall now be reaped with joy. The

Word of the Lord shall not re - turn __ void.

Cast out your nets, all ye fish - ers of men. In the

pow'r of the Spir - it, re - viv - al __ be - gin!

Medley options: Jehovah-Jireh; Trees of the Field.

God is our refuge and strength, a very present help in trouble. Psalm 46:1

God Is My Refuge

Words and Music by
JUDY HORNER MONTEMAYOR

God is my ref-uge, and God is my strength; A ver-y pres-ent help in troub-le.

God is my ref-uge, and God is my strength; A ver-y pres-ent help in troub-le.

Medley options: Chosen Generation; Let Your Spirit Rise.

God Is the Strength of My Heart

Wor...
EU...

Medley options: He Who Began a Good Work; Almighty.

I will even make a roadway in the wilderness, rivers in the desert. Isaiah 43:19

52 God Will Make a Way

Words and Music by
DON MOEN

Medley options: Be Magnified; Amazing Grace.

As the dawn is spread over the mountains, so there is a great and mighty people. Joel 2:2

Great and Mighty Army   53

Words and Music by
RANDY AND DANA ROTHWELL

CHORUS

shout, let's shout the vic - to - ry! The en - e - my is un - der our feet. So let's shout, let's shout the vic - to - ry! For great is our King, great is our King,___ great___ is the King___ of kings.

Medley options: Make a Joyful Noise; Ah, Lord God.

Great is the Lord, and greatly to be praised. Psalm 48:1

54

Great and Mighty Is He

Words and Music by
TODD PETTYGROVE

Medley options: Mighty Is Our God; My Help Comes From the Lord.

...l, and greatly to be praised, in the city of our God,
...ntain...the joy of the whole earth. Psalm 48:1,2

eat Is the Lord

Words and Music by
STEVE McEWAN

Great is the Lord__ and most wor-thy of

praise, the cit-y of our God, the ho-ly

place. the joy of the__ whole earth.__

Great is the

Lord, we want to thank You for the works You've done in our lives: And

Lord we trust in Your un-fail-ing love. For

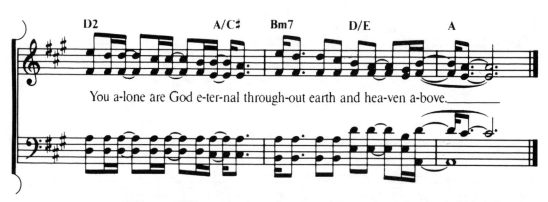

You a-lone are God e-ter-nal through-out earth and hea-ven a-bove.

Medley options: Joy of My Desire; I Stand in Awe.

Hallelujah! Our God Reigns

Hallelujah! For the Lord our God, the Almighty reigns. Revelation

Words and
DALE GARR

Medley options: The Spirit of the Lord..

Thine is the dominion, O Lord. 1 Chronicles 29:11

He Is Exalted

Words and Music by
TWILA PARIS

He is ex - alt - ed, the King is ex - alt - ed on high. I will praise_ Him. He is ex - alt - ed, for ev - er ex - alt - ed and I will praise His name!_____

CHORUS

He is the Lord. For-ev-er His truth shall

reign.___ Heav-en and earth___ re -

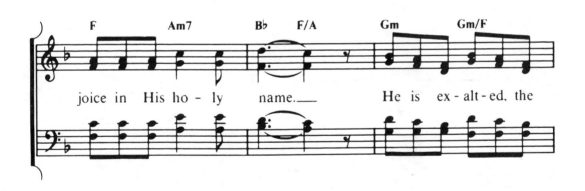

joice in His ho-ly name.___ He is ex-alt-ed, the

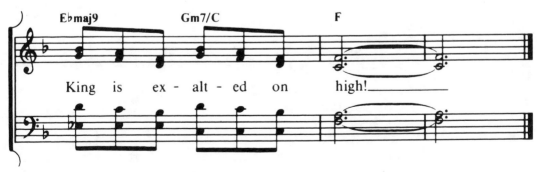

King is ex-alt-ed on high!___

Medley options: We Bow Down; Under the Blood.

58

He Is Lovely

Words and Music by
BOB FITTS

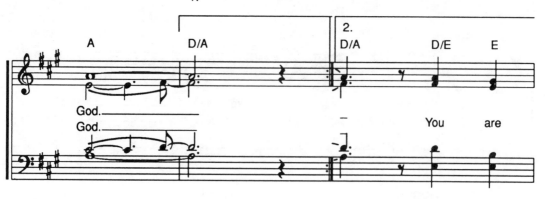

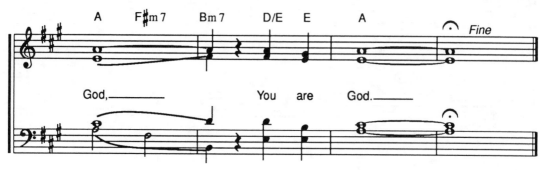

Medley options: Come Into the Holy of Holies.

He who is the blessed and only Sovereign, the King of kings and Lord of lords. 1 Timothy 6:15
And on His robe and on His thigh He has a name written,
"KING OF KINGS AND LORD OF LORDS." Revelation 19:16

He Is the King of Kings

59

Words and Music by
VIRGIL MEARES

He is the King of kings, He is the
Lord of lords; His name is Je-sus, Je-sus,
Je-sus, Je-sus, Oh,— He is the King. He is the King.

Medley options: My Glory and the Lifter of My Head; Chosen Generation.

60

He Who Began
a Good Work

Words and Music by
JON MOHR

CMaj 7 Bm 7

has His hand on you, safe and se - cure, He will

Am 7   D2 D

nev - er a - ban - don you. You are His trea - sure, and

D9 D7 G Bm 7 Am 7 *D.C. al Coda*
              Am 7/D

He finds His plea - sure in you.

Coda   *Fine*
G

Medley options: God Is the Strength of My Heart.

Hear my cry, O God; give heed to my prayer. Psalm 61:1

Hear My Cry

61

Author Unknown

Hear my cry, O Lord,_ at - tend un - to_____ my_
For_ Thou hast been_ a shel - ter un - to_

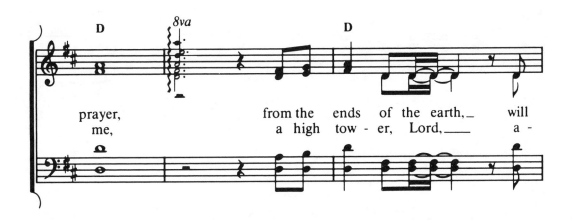

prayer,
me,

from the ends of the earth,_ will
a high tow - er, Lord,_____ a -

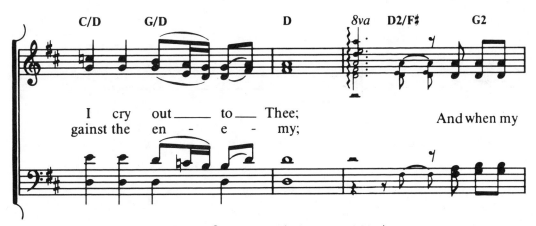

I cry out _____ to _ Thee;
gainst the en - e - my;

And when my

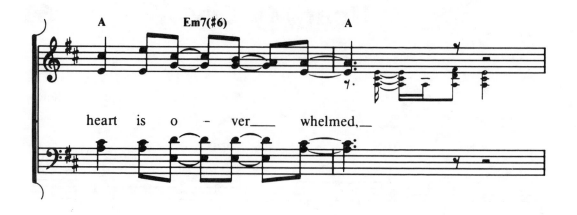

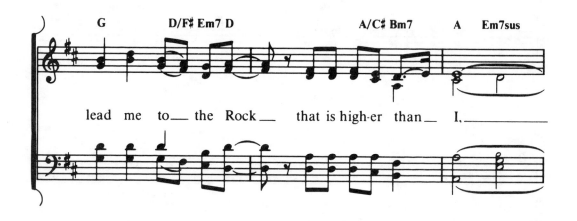

Medley options: Be Glorified; Change My Heart, Oh God.

Heaven Is in My Heart

62

Words and Music by
GRAHAM KENDRICK

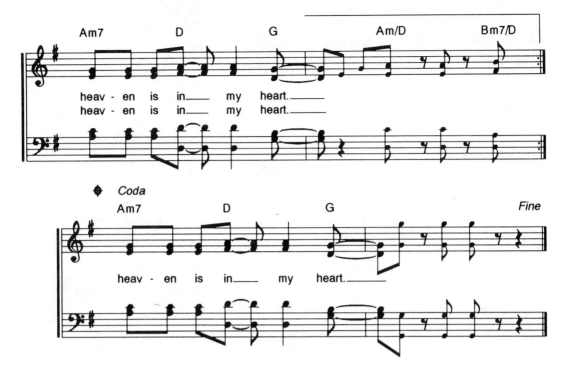

Medley options: Why So Downcast; Let the Heavens Rejoice.

63

Now to Him who is able to keep you from stumbling, and to make you stand in the presence of His glory blameless with great joy. Jude 24

Here We Are

Words and Music by
DALLAS HOLM

Medley options: I Want to Be Where You Are; I Worship You.

Therefore God exalted Him to the highest place and gave Him the name that is above every name. Philippians 2:9

Highest Place

64

Words and Music by
RAMON PINK

Lyrics:
We place You on the high-est place, for You are the great High Priest; We place You high a-bove all else, and we come to You

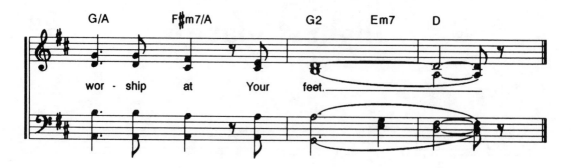

Medley options: I Want to Be More Like You; More Than Anything.

Holy Ground

65

Words and Music by
GERON DAVIS

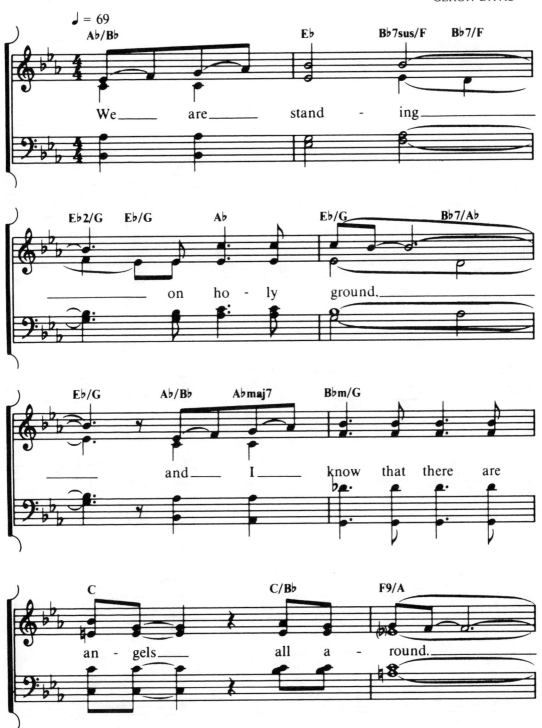

We are stand-ing on ho-ly ground. and I know that there are an-gels all a-round.

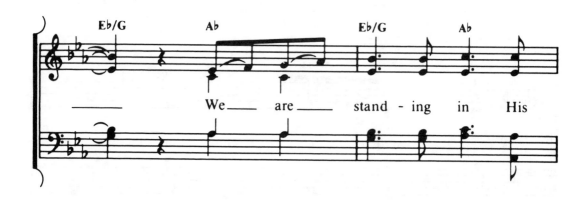

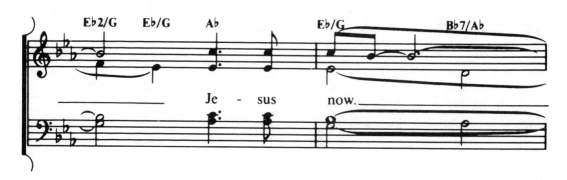

Medley options: Come Into the King's Chambers; More Precious Than Silver.

Blessed is He who comes in the name of the Lord; Hosanna in the highest! Matthew 21:9

Hosanna

Words and Music by
CARL TUTTLE

Medley options: Arise and Sing; Firm Foundation.

O Lord, our Lord, how excellent is Thy name in all the earth. Psalm 8:1

67 How Excellent Is Thy Name

Words and Music by
DICK and MELODIE TUNNEY and PAUL SMITH

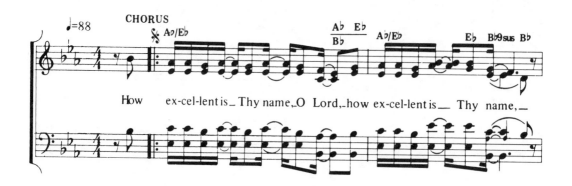

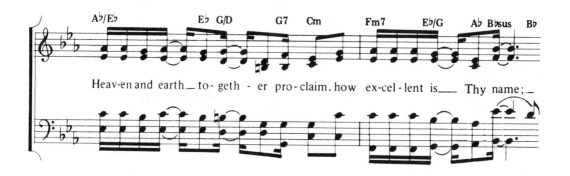

reign - ing maj - es - ty,__ and yet I find__ You take the time__ to

care for one__ like me._____ How

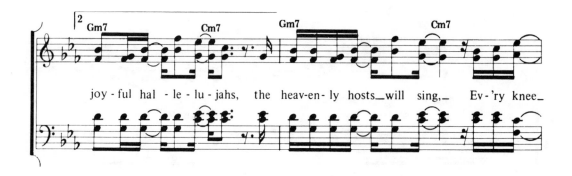

joy - ful hal - le - lu - jahs, the heav - en - ly hosts__will sing,__ Ev - 'ry knee__

__ shall bow, ev - 'ry tongue__will__shout.__You're the King__of kings. _____ How

Medley options: Lord of All.

It is good to give thanks to the Lord. Psalm 92:1

How Good It Is

68

Words and Music by
DANNY CHAMBERS

How good it___ is to give thanks___ un-to the___ Lord, how good it___ is to give thanks___ un-to our God;___ O, He heals the bro-ken-heart-ed, bind-ing up___ their___wounds,___ it is good___ to bless___ His ho-ly

ev - er,   and   I will wor - ship Him___ all of___ my

days._____   How   good   it___   name._____

Medley options: Lord of All; Clap Your Hands.

69

...may have power, together with all the saints, to grasp how wide and long and high and deep is the love of Christ. Ephesians 3:18

How Great Is Your Love
(How High and How Wide)

Words and Music by
MARK ALTROGGE

♩ = 160   **VERSE**

1. No eye___ has seen ♩ and no ear___ has heard, and
2. Ob-jects___ of mer-cy,___ who should have___ known wrath, we're

no mind___ has ev-er con-ceived___ the glo-ri-ous
filled with___ un-speak-a-ble joy,___ ♩ rich-es___ of

things ♩ that You have___ pre-pared for___ ev-'ry-one
wis-dom___ un-search-a-ble wealth, and the won-der___ of

who has___ be-lieved;___ You brought___ us near and___ You
know-ing___ Your voice;___ You are___ our treas-ure___ and

Medley options: My Life Is in You, Lord; Let the Heavens Rejoice.

For I, the Lord, am your healer. Exodus 15:26

I Am the God That Healeth Thee

Words and Music by
DON MOEN

1. I am the God— that heal-eth— thee,—
2. You are the God— that heal-eth— me,—

I am the Lord,— your Heal-er;
You are the Lord,— my Heal-er;

I sent My word and healed your dis-ease.—
You sent Your word and healed my dis-ease,—

I am the Lord,— your Heal-er.
You are the Lord,— my Heal-er.

Medley options: Blessed Be the Name of the Lord; Worthy, You Are Worthy.

I Believe in Jesus

71

Words and Music by
MARC NELSON

Medley options: I Was Made to Praise You; Exalt the Lord Our God.

72   I Bow My Knee

Words and Music by
BONNIE DEUSCHLE

Medley options: I Stand in Awe; Exalted; Be Glorified.

I Exalt Thee

73

Words and Music by
PETE SANCHEZ, JR.

For Thou, Oh Lord, art high a-bove all the earth,____ Thou art ex - alt - ed far a - bove all____ gods; For Thou, Oh Lord, art high a-bove all the earth,____ Thou art ex -

Medley options: Thou Art Worthy, Great Jehovah; All Hail King Jesus.

I will extol Thee, my God, O King. Psalm 145:1

I Extol You

74

Words and Music by
JENNIFER RANDOLPH

Prince of Peace, Coun-se-lor,___ mer-ci-ful___ Son of God, Lord of Hosts, Con-quer-or, Com-ing King and Ev-er-liv-ing God,___ I ex-

CHORUS

Medley options: I Sing Praises; No Other Name.

I Love to Be in Your Presence

75

Words and Music by
PAUL BALOCHE and ED KERR

I love to be in Your pres - ence, with Your peo-ple sing-ing prais - es; I love to stand and re - joice, lift my hands and raise my voice. I

VERSE

You set my feet to danc - ing, You fill my heart with song;

Medley options: Glory, Glory Lord; The Spirit of the Lord.

Let my soul live that it may praise Thee. Psalm 119:175

I Love to Praise Him 76

Words and Music by
JENNIFER RANDOLPH

I love to praise Him,

I love to praise Him; I love to praise

Him And lift up His holy name.

Medley options: Blessed Be the Rock; O, Clap Your Hands.

I saw the Lord sitting on a throne, high and lifted up,
and the train of His robe filled the temple. Isaiah 6:1

77

I See the Lord

Words and Music by
JON CHISUM and DON MOEN

I see the Lord, I see the Lord ex-alt-ed high up-on__ the wor - ship__ of the peo-ple of__ the earth;__ I see the Lord, I see the Lord,___ my eyes have seen__ the King,___ the Lamb up-on__ the throne__

Medley options: To Him Who Sits on the Throne; Glory to the Lamb.

Therefore I will give thanks to Thee among the nations, O Lord,
and I will sing praises to Thy name. Psalm 18:49

I Sing Praises

Words and Music by
TERRY MacALMON

♩ = 69

1. I sing prais-es to Your name, O Lord, prais-es to Your
(2. I give glo-ry to Your) name, O Lord, glo-ry to Your

name, O Lord, for Your name is great and great-ly to be
name, O Lord, for Your name is great and great-ly to be

praised; I sing prais-es to Your name, O Lord, prais-es to Your
I give glo-ry to Your name, O Lord, glo-ry to Your

name, O Lord, for Your name is great and
name, O Lord, for Your name is great and

1. great-ly to be praised. 2. I give glo-ry to Your
2. praised.

Medley options: I Extol You; Forever Grateful.

Let all the inhabitants of the world stand in awe of Him. Psalm 33:8

I Stand in Awe

Words and Music by
MARK ALTROGGE

You are beau-ti-ful—— be-yond de-scrip-tion, too mar-ve-lous—— for words,—— too won-der-ful for com-pre-hen sion,—— like noth-ing ev-er seen or heard.—— Who can grasp Your in-fin-ite—— wis-dom, who can

fath-om the depth of Your love?____ You are

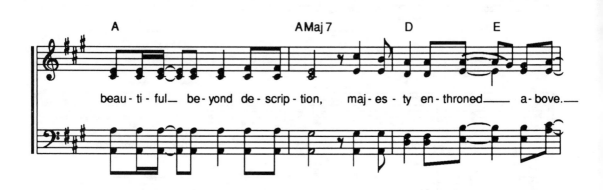

beau-ti-ful_ be-yond de-scrip-tion, maj-es-ty en-throned___ a-bove._

CHORUS

_ And I stand, I_ stand in awe of You, I stand, I_ stand in

awe of You;_ ho-ly God, to Whom all praise is due, I

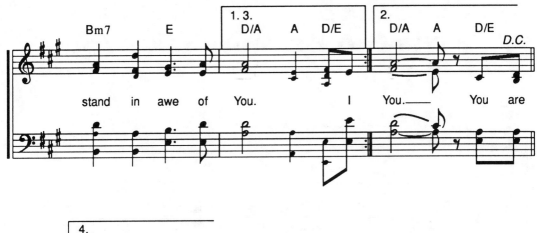

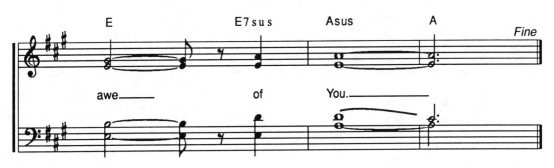

Medley options: I Will Magnify; Salvation Belongs to Our God; Great Is the Lord.

80

I Want to Be More Like You

Words and Music by
CLINT BROWN

Medley options: More Than Anything; Sanctuary.

I Want to Be
Where You Are

81

Words and Music by
DON MOEN

2nd time to Coda

Medley options: Here We Are; Blessed Be the Name of the Lord.

I will give thanks to Thee, for I am fearfully and wonderfully made. Psalm 139:14

I Was Made to Praise You 82

Words and Music by
CHRIS CHRISTENSEN

I____ was made to praise____ You,
I____ will al - ways praise____ You, I____ was made to
I____ will al - ways

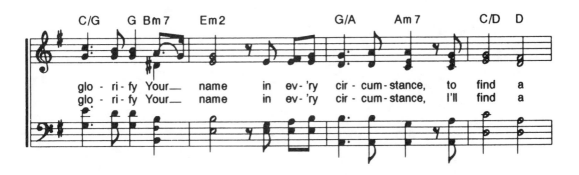

glo - ri - fy Your____ name in ev - 'ry cir - cum - stance, to find a
glo - ri - fy Your____ name in ev - 'ry cir - cum - stance, I'll find a

chance to thank You.____ I was made to love____ You,
chance to thank You.____ I will al - ways love____ You,

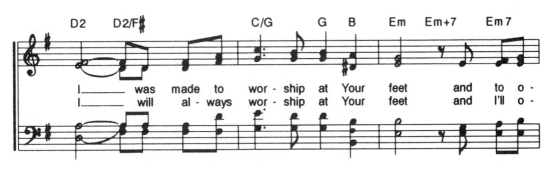

I____ was made to wor - ship at Your feet and to o -
I____ will al - ways wor - ship at Your feet and I'll o -

Medley options: Give Thanks; I Bow My Knee.

Arise, go down against the camp, for I have given it into your hands. Judges 7:9

I Will Arise

83

Words and Music by
LESLIE BROWN

I will a- rise and go forth in the name____ of the Lord of hosts,__ for He has con- quered__ eve- ry foe____ by His name,_____ by His name.____ I will de-

Medley options: Let Your Spirit Rise; God Is My Refuge.

I will bless the Lord at all times. Psalm 34:1

I Will Bless the Lord

84

Words and Music by
FRANK HERNANDEZ

Medley options: Worthy the Lamb That Was Slain; Thou Art Worthy.

85 I Will Bless Thee, O Lord

I will bless Thee as long as I live;
I will lift up my hands in Thy name. Psalm 63:4

Words and Music by
ESTHER WATANABE

♩. = 54

VERSE

With my hands lift - ed up____ and my mouth filled with praise.____ with a heart of thanks - giv - ing,____ I will bless Thee, O Lord.____

Medley options: Jesus, Name Above All Names..

I call upon the Lord, who is worthy to be praised...
The Lord lives! Blessed be my Rock! Psalm 18:3,46

I Will Call Upon the Lord

Words and Music by
MICHAEL O'SHIELDS

(Men) I will call up-on the Lord,
(Women) I will call up-on the Lord,

Lord,
Who is wor-thy to be praised. Who is wor-thy to be

praised.
So shall I be saved from my en-e-mies. So shall I be

saved from my en-e-mies.
The Lord liv-eth and

Medley options: Why So Downcast?; Righteousness, Peace, Joy.

Come let us worship and bow down. Psalm 95:6

87 I Will Come and Bow Down

Words and Music by
MARTIN J. NYSTROM

Medley options: Let There Be Glory and Honor and Praises; In Moments Like These.

I will praise the name of God with song, and shall
magnify Him with thanksgiving. Psalm 69:30

I Will Magnify

88

Words and Music by
RUSSELL L. LOWE

Fa - ther, cre - a - tor of all____ things.____

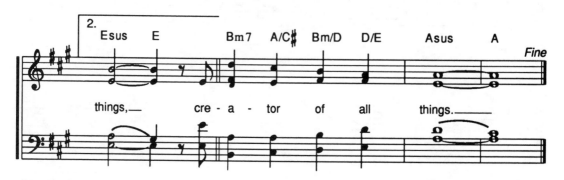

things,__ cre - a - tor of all things.____

Medley options: I Stand in Awe; Salvation Belongs to Our God; Great Is the Lord.

I Will Sing of the Mercies of the Lord

89

Words and Music by
J. H. FILLMORE

I will sing of the mer-cies of the Lord for-ev-er, I will sing,_____ I will sing;_____ I will sing of the mer-cies of the Lord for-ev-er, I will sing of the mer-cies of the Lord._____ With my mouth_____ will I make known Thy faith-ful-ness,_____ Thy faith-ful-ness;_____ With my mouth_____ will I make known Thy

Medley options: Come Into His Presence; My Glory and the Lifter of My Head.

O Lord, there is none like Thee. 1 Chronicles 17:20

I Worship You, Almighty God

90

Words and Music by
SONDRA CORBETT

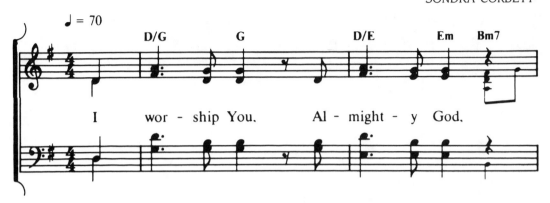

I wor - ship You, Al - might - y God,

there is none like You. I wor - ship You, O

Prince of Peace, that is what I want to do. I

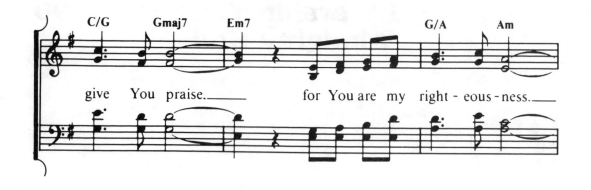

give You praise.____ for You are my right - eous - ness.____

____ I wor - ship You. Al -

might - y God, there is none like You.

Medley options: Exalt the Lord Our God; Spirit of the Living God.

For in Him we live and move and exist. Acts 17:28

In Him We Live

91

Words and Music by
RANDY SPEIR

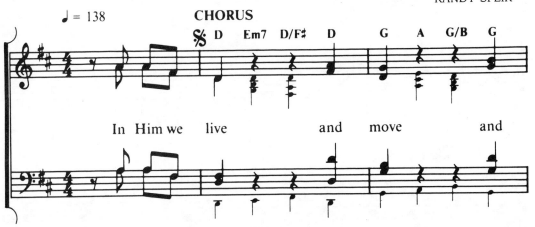

fine

have our be - ing.

VERSE

Make a joy - ful noise! Sing un-to__ the Lord!

1.

Tell Him of__ your love, dance be - fore Him.

2.

D.S. al fine

Hal - le - lu - jah!_____ In Him we

Medley options: We Bring the Sacrifice of Praise; Ah, Lord God; Let the Redeemed.

I love the Lord, because He hears my voice. Psalm 116:1

In Moments Like These   92

Words and Music by
DAVID GRAHAM

In mo-ments like these I sing out a song,— I sing out a love song to Je-sus; In mo-ments like these — I lift up my hands, I lift up my hands to the Lord. Sing-ing

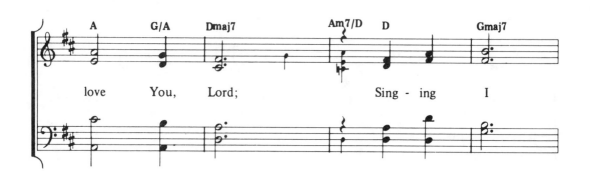

Medley options: Thou Art Worthy; I Will Come and Bow Down.

*Holy, holy, holy is the Lord God, the Almighty, who was
and who is and who is to come. Revelation 4:8*

93

In the Presence

Words and Music by
MARK ALTROGGE

Medley options: I Extol You; I Sing Praises.

In Your presence is fullness of joy; at Your
right hand are pleasures forevermore. Psalm 16:11

In Your Presence

Words and Music by
BILLY FUNK and MARTIN J. NYSTROM

In Your pres-ence__ there is ful-ness__ of joy,__ at your
right hand__ there are pleas-ures ev - er-more;__ You sur-
round us__ with Your fa-vor,__ O Lord,__ the earth is full of Your
good - ness, the earth is filled with Your__ love. Ex -

Medley options: Such Joy; Lift Him Up.

Offer yourselves to God. . .as instruments of righteousness. Romans 6:13

Instruments of Your Peace 95

Words and Music by
KIRK and DEBY DEARMAN

Lord, make us in-stru-ments of your peace; Where there is ha-tred let Your love in-crease.__ Lord, make us in-stru-ments of your peace; Walls of pride and prej-u-dice shall__ cease,__ when we are Your in-stru-ments__ of peace.__

Medley options: We Are An Offering; Create In Me A Clean Heart.

In the mount of the Lord it will be provided. Genesis 22:14

Jehovah-Jireh

96

Words and Music by
MERLA WATSON

Je-ho-vah Ji-reh,___ my Pro-vid-er,___ His grace is suf-fi-cient for___ me, for me,___ for me;

Je-ho-vah Ji-reh,___ my Pro-vid-er,___ His grace is suf-fi-cient for___ me. My

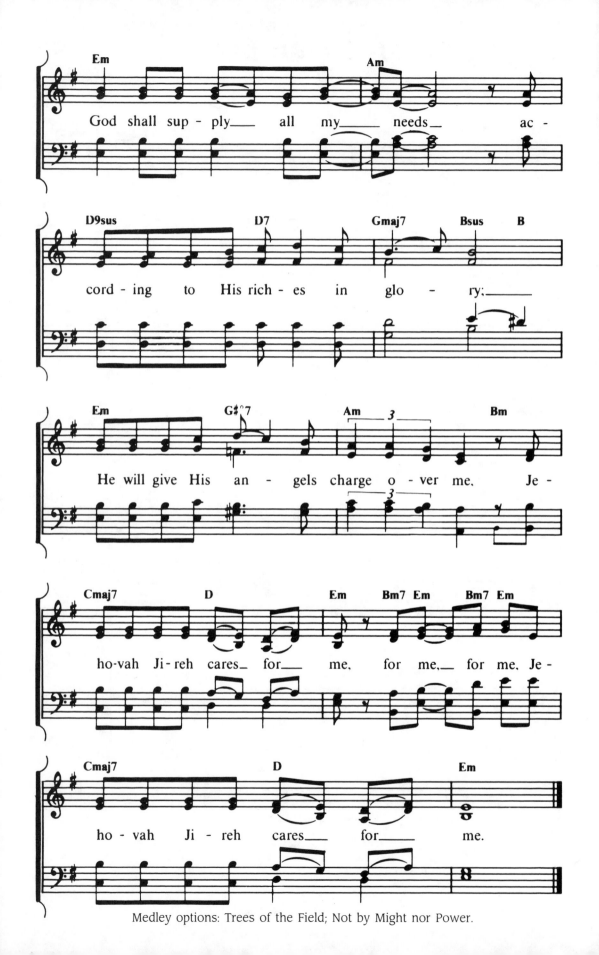

Medley options: Trees of the Field; Not by Might nor Power.

He is not here, for He has risen, just as He said. Matthew 28:6

Jesus Is Alive

97

Words and Music by
RON KENOLY

Hal - le - lu - jah! Je - sus is a - live, death has lost its vic - t'ry and the grave has been de - nied; Je - sus lives for - ev - er, He's a-

Medley options: Making War in the Heavenlies; The Lord Is Come.

98

Jesus, Name Above All Names

Words and Music by
NAIDA HEARN

Medley options: I Will Bless Thee, O Lord.

Joy of My Desire

99

Words and Music by
JENNIFER RANDOLPH

CHORUS

I wor-ship You in spir-it and in___ truth.___ I wor-ship You in spir-it and in___ truth. There will ne-ver be a friend as dear to me as You.____

Medley options: Blessed Be the Lord God Almighty; Great Is the Lord.

Behold, the Lamb of God who takes away the sin of the world! John 1:29

Lamb of God

100

Words and Music by
TWILA PARIS

1. Your on - ly Son, no sin to hide; but You have sent Him from Your__ side_____ to walk up - on this guilt - y sod_____ and to be - come the Lamb of
(2. Your gift of) love they cru - ci - fied. They laughed and scorned Him as He____ died._____ The hum - ble King they named a fraud_____ and sac - ri - ficed the Lamb of
(3. I was so) lost, I should have died; but You have brought me to Your__ side_____ to be led by Your staff and rod_____ and to be called a lamb of

Medley options: Amazing Grace.

Let everything that has breath praise the Lord. Psalm 150:6

101

Let Everything
That Has Breath

Words and Music by
RICH GOMEZ

Medley options: Lift Him Up; Clap Your Hands.

102 Let God Arise

Words and Music by
ELIZABETH BACON

Medley options: Let Your Spirit Rise; I Will Arise.

Let the Heavens Rejoice   103

Words and Music by
DON HARRIS and MARTIN J. NYSTROM

Let the heav - ens re - joice and the earth be__ glad,

let the seas__ re - sound__ with a might - y

roar; Let the trees__ of the for - est clap their

hands, let the earth be filled__ with the

Medley options: Heaven Is in My Heart; How Great Is Your Love.

Let the redeemed of the Lord say so. Psalm 107:2

Let the Redeemed

104

Words and Music by
WARD ELLIS

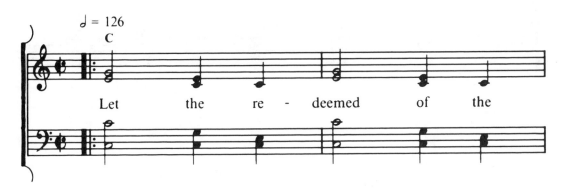

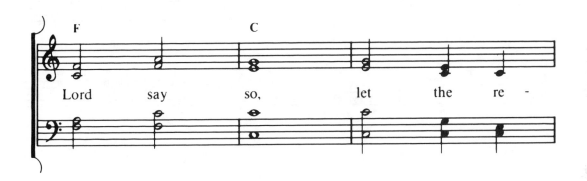

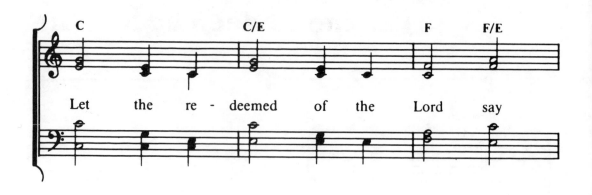

Let the re - deemed of the Lord say

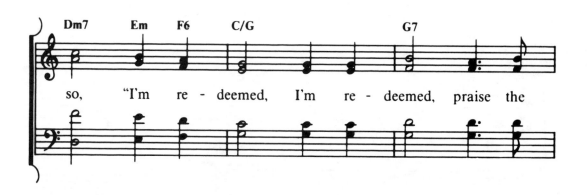

so, "I'm re - deemed, I'm re - deemed, praise the

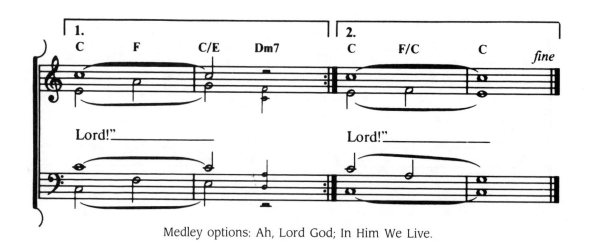

Lord!"_____   Lord!"_____

Medley options: Ah, Lord God; In Him We Live.

Let There Be Glory and Honor and Praises

105

Words and Music by
JAMES and ELIZABETH GREENELSH

Let there be glo - ry and hon - or and prais - es; Glo - ry and hon - or to Je - sus. Glo - ry and hon - or, glo - ry and hon - or to

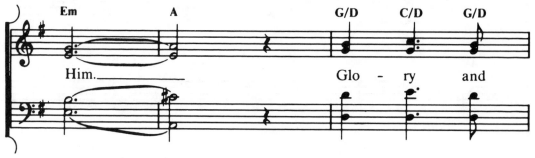

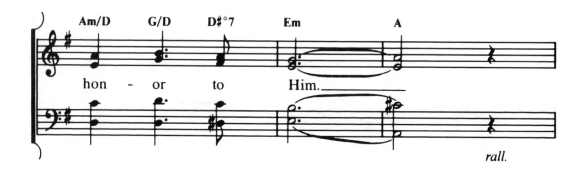

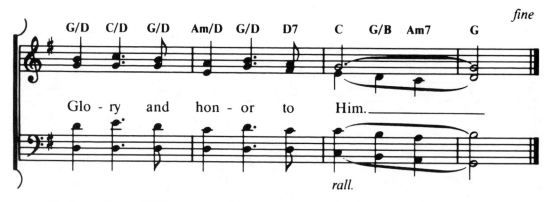

Medley options: I Will Come and Bow Down; Worthy the Lamb That Was Slain.

But the fruit of the Spirit is...joy. Galatians 5:22

Let Your Spirit Rise Within Me

106

Words and Music by
RANDY SPEIR

Let Your Spir-it rise with-in me,

let Your Spir-it rise with-in me. You set my

feet a danc-in' and my heart re-joic-in' and my

mouth sing-in' out Your praise.

Let Your Spir-it rise with-in me,

let Your Spir-it rise with-in me. You set my

feet a danc- in' and my heart re- joic- in' and my

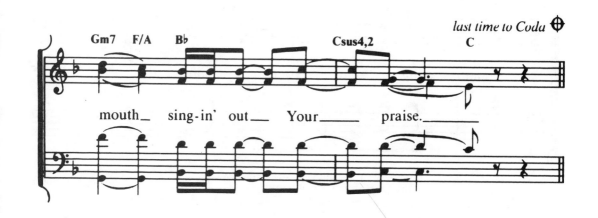

last time to Coda

mouth— sing-in' out— Your——— praise.———————

Medley options: I Will Arise; God Is My Refuge; He Is the King of Kings.

107

I wait for the Lord, my soul does wait, and in His word do I hope. Psalm 130:5

Let's Take Time

Words and Music by
MARY WETZEL FREEMAN

1. Let's take time to wait up-on the Lord, let's take time to lis-ten to His voice; Un-less the Lord builds the house they la-bor in vain, so let's take time to wait up-on the Lord.
2. Let's take time to wait up-on the Lord, let's take time to feed up-on His Word; Un-less the Lord builds the house they la-bor in vain, so let's take time to wait up-on the Lord.

Medley options: Your Steadfast Love; O Lord, You're Beautiful.

And Moses built an altar, and named it The Lord Is My Banner. Exodus 17:15

Lift High the Lord Our Banner

108

Words and Music by
MACON DELAVAN

Lift high the Lord, our Ban-ner. Lift high the

Lord, Je-sus King. Lift high the Lord, our Ban-ner. Lift high your

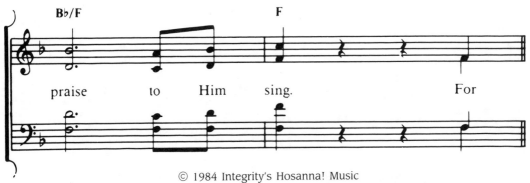

praise to Him sing. For

Medley options: Mighty Warrior; Above All Else.

...Let every creature praise His holy name for ever and ever. Psalm 145:21

Lift Him Up

109

Words and Music by
BILLY FUNK

I will come___ in-to Your pres-ence, Lord,___
I will give___ you all the glo - ry,___

with a sac - ri - fice of praise;___
you de-liv - ered me from shame;___

With a song___ I will ex - alt You, Lord,___
I'm cre - at - ed in Your right - eous - ness,___

bless-ed be___ Your ho-ly name.___
bless-ed be___ Your ho-ly name.___

Medley options: Be Exalted; Clap, Clap Your Hands.

I will yet praise Him, the help of my countenance. Psalm 42:11

Lift Up Your Countenance

110

Words and Music by
RICHARD RILEY

Lift up your coun-te-nance, all ye saints of God, lift up your coun-te-nance, for the vic-to-ry is won; Lift up your coun-te-nance, all ye saints of God, and give the glo-ry to the Ho-ly One. Lift up your

Medley options: The Name of the Lord; Rejoice in the Lord.

Lift up your heads...your redemption is drawing near. Luke 21:28

Lift Up Your Heads

111

Words and Music by
STEVEN L. FRY

Lift up your heads to the com - ing King. Bow be - fore Him and a - dore Him, sing.

Medley options: Thou Art Worthy, Great Jehovah; All Hail King Jesus.

Like a Shepherd

112

Words and Music by
DON MOEN and DEBORAH SIMPSON

1. Like a fa-ther feeds__ his chil-dren, like a
2. (As we) come in-to__ His pres-ence __ con-

shep-herd leads__ his flock,__ the
fess-ing Him__ as Lord,__ His

Lord will al-ways guide__ us__ and
Ho-ly Spir-it leads__ us,__ He

show us where to walk;__ And in
feeds us by His Word;__ We're__

Medley options: My Soul Follows Hard After Thee; Lord, I'm Gonna Love You.

Lion of Judah

113

Words and Music by
TED SANDQUIST

♩ = 87

1.,4. Li - on of Ju - dah on the throne,
2. Li - on of Ju - dah, come to earth,
3. Li - on of Ju - dah, come a - gain.

I shout Your Name;_ let it ___ be known that You are the
I want to thank _ You for _ Your birth, ___ for Your
Take up Your throne, Je - ru - sa - lem. ___ Bring re -

King of ___ kings, ___ You are the Prince _ of Peace. May Your
liv - ing ___ Word, ___ for Your death _ on ___ the tree, for Your
lease to this earth ___ and the con - sum - ma-tion of Your

Medley options: Mighty Warrior.

Lord, I'm Gonna Love You

114

Words and Music by
KEITH GREEN

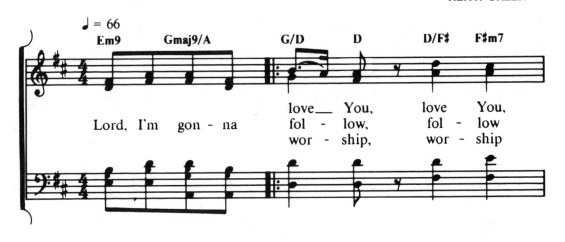

You
You with all that's in my___ heart, _____
You

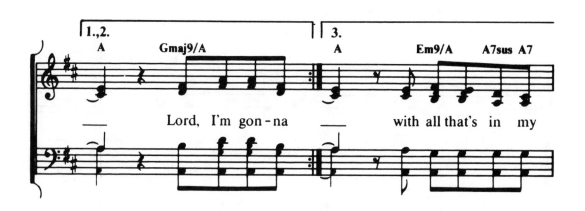

1.,2. ___ Lord, I'm gon-na ___ 3. with all that's in my

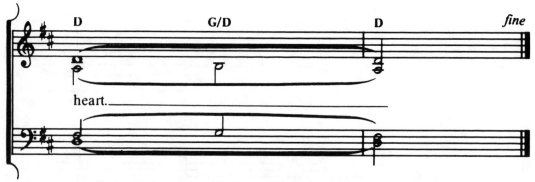

heart. _____

Medley options: My Soul Follows Hard After Thee; Like a Shepherd.

Lord of All

115

Words and Music by
STEVE ISRAEL and GERRIT GUSTAFSON

Medley options: Clap Your Hands; Above All Else.

116

*Shout joyfully to God, all the earth; sing the glory of
His name; make His praise glorious. Psalm 66:1*

Make a Joyful Noise

Words and Music by
RUSSELL L. LOWE

CHORUS

Wor - thy, wor - thy,
He is wor - thy to be praised. —
Hal - le - lu - jah, Our
God is great - ly to be praised. —

Medley options: Not by Might nor Power; Jehovah Jireh.

We are destroying speculations and every lofty thing raised up against the knowledge of God, and we are taking every thought captive to the obedience of Christ. 2 Corinthians 10:5

117

Making War in the Heavenlies

Words and Music by
GEORGE SEARCY

Mak - ing war___ in the heav - en - lies, tear - ing down___ prin - ci - pal - i - ties, stand - ing firm___ in Je - sus' vic - to - ry;___ Mak - ing war___ in the heav - en - lies, cast - ing down___ ev - 'ry high thing

Medley options: Jesus Is Alive; The Lord Is Come.

The Lord on high is mighty. Psalm 93:4

118 Mighty Is Our God

Words and Music by
EUGENE GRECO, GERRIT GUSTAFSON
and DON MOEN

Might-y is our God, might-y is our King;
Might-y is our Lord, rul-er of ev-'ry-thing.
Glo-ry to our God, glo-ry to our King;

Medley options: My Help Comes From the Lord; Great and Mighty Is He.

The Lord is a warrior... Exodus 15:3

119 **Mighty Warrior**

Words and Music by
DEBBYE GRAAFSMA

Might-y War - rior, dressed for bat - tle, ho - ly Lord of all is He.

Com-man - der in chief, bring us to at - ten - tion, lead us in - to bat - tle to crush the en - e - my.

VERSE

Sa - tan has no au - thor - i - ty
Je - sus all

here in this place, He has no all au - thor - i - ty here. For

this hab - i - ta - tion __ was fash-ioned for the Lord's pre-sence,

no all au - thor - i - ty here. ____

Medley options: Lift High the Lord Our Banner; Above All Else.

120

More Love, More Power

Words and Music by
JUDE DEL HIERRO

Medley options: Awesome God; All Consuming Fire.

There is none upon earth that I desire besides You. Psalm 73:25

121 More of You

Words and Music by
DON HARRIS and MARTIN J. NYSTROM

Je-sus I am thirst-y, won't You come and fill___ me? Earth-ly things have left me dry,___ on-ly You can sat-is-fy,___ all I want is more___ of You. All I want is more of You,___ all I want is more of You;___ Noth-ing I de-

Medley options: I Was Made to Praise You; On Bended Knee.

122
More Precious
Than Silver

Words and Music by
LYNN DeSHAZO

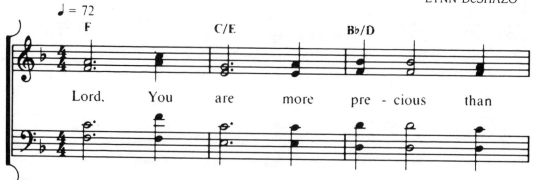

Lord, You are more pre - cious than

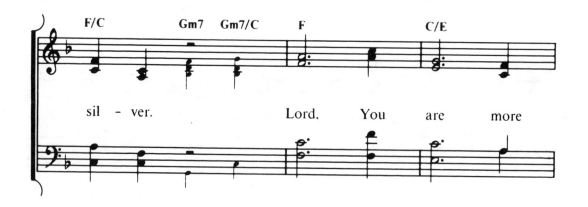

sil - ver. Lord, You are more

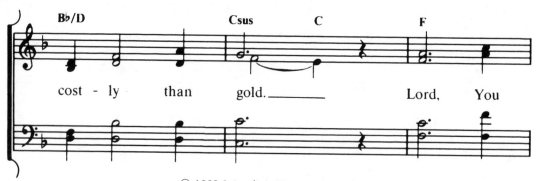

cost - ly than gold._____ Lord, You

are _____ more beau - ti - ful _____ than

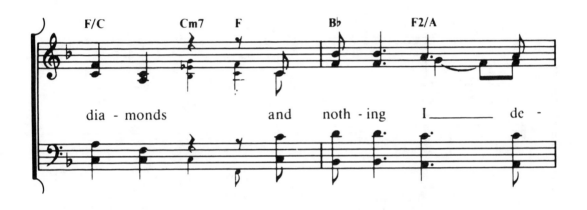

dia - monds and noth - ing I _____ de -

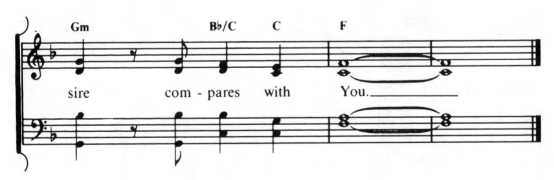

sire com - pares with You. _____

Medley options: Thou Art Worthy, Great Jehovah; I Worship You, Almighty God.

Whom have I in heaven but Thee? And besides Thee,
I desire nothing on earth. Psalm 73:25

More Than Anything

Words and Music by
CHRIS CHRISTENSEN

♩ = 104

CHORUS

1. More than an-y-thing, more than an-y-thing,
2.&3. More than an-y-thing, more than an-y-thing,

I love You, Je-sus, more than an-y-thing;___
I love You, Je-sus, more than an-y-thing;___

More than an-y-thing, more than an-y-thing,
More than world-ly wealth, more than life it-self,

I love You, Je-sus, more than an-y-thing.
I love You, Je-sus, more than an-y-thing.

Medley options: O Lord, You're Beautiful; More Precious Than Silver.

124 More Than Conquerors

Words and Music by
BILL and JANNY GREIN

Medley options: Be Strong and Take Courage.

You turned my wailing into dancing . . .that my heart
may sing to You and not be silent. Psalm 30:11,12

Mourning Into Dancing

Words and Music by
TOMMY WALKER

Lyrics:

He's turned my mourn - ing in - to danc - ing a - gain, He's lift - ed my sor - rows;

And I can't stay si - lent, I must sing for His joy has come.

VERSE 1

Where there once was on-ly__ hurt,__

__ He gave His heal-ing__ hand;_____ Where there

once was on-ly__ pain,_____ He brought com-fort like a__ friend.__

__ I feel the sweet-ness of His__ love_____ pierc-ing my

dark-ness;_____ I see the bright and morn-ing__ sun__

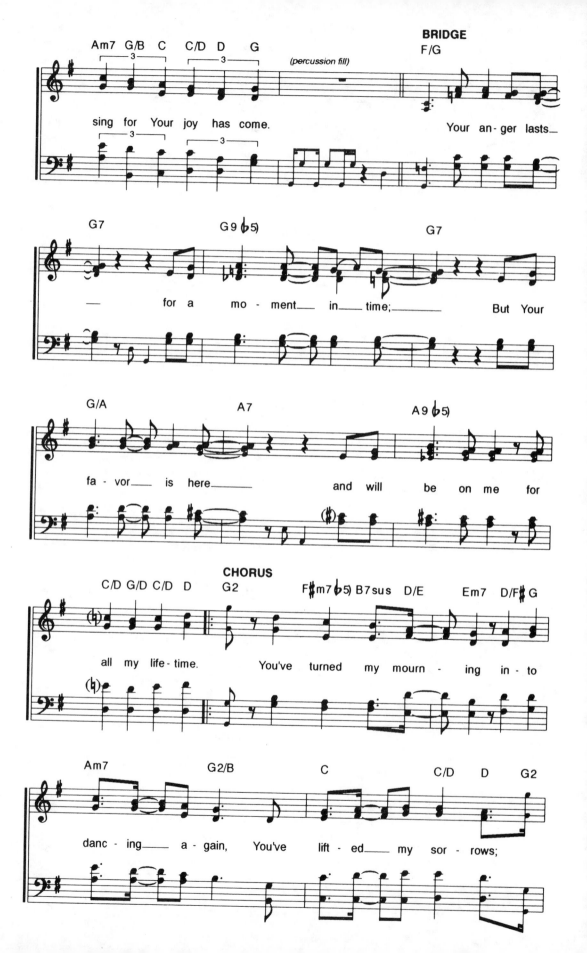

Medley options: I Love to Praise Him.

126

My Glory and the Lifter of My Head

Words and Music by
MAE McALISTER

♩ = 128

CHORUS

C   **F/C**   **C**

My Glo - ry and the Lift - er of my head,   My

F/C   **C**   **G**   **C**   **C/Bb**

Glo - ry and the Lift - er of my head, For Thou, Oh Lord, art a

F/A   **C/G**   **F**   **Dm7**   **G**   *1.* **C**

Shield for me, My Glo - ry and the Lift - er of my head. My

VERSE

2 **C**   **Dm**   **C/E**   **C**   **G7**   **C**

head.   I cried un - to the Lord with my voice,_____ I

Medley options: He Is the King of Kings; Let the Redeemed.

My help comes from the Lord, who made heaven and earth. Psalm 121:2

127 My Help Comes From the Lord

Words and Music by
STEPHEN BRAY, DON MOEN
and MARTIN J. NYSTROM

Medley options: Mighty Is Our God; Great and Mighty Is He; Celebrate Jesus.

And you shall love the Lord your God with all your heart and with all your soul and with all your might. Deuteronomy 6:5

My Life Is in You, Lord

128

Words and Music by
DANIEL GARDNER

Medley options: Celebrate Jesus; This Is the Day.

My soul clings to Thee, Thy right hand upholds me. Psalm 63:8

My Soul Follows Hard After Thee

129

Words and Music by
JEFFREY SMITH

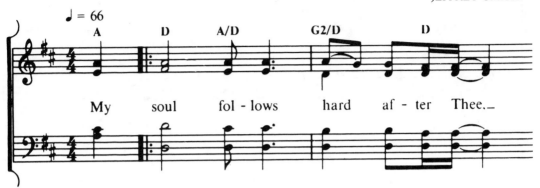

My soul fol - lows hard af - ter Thee._

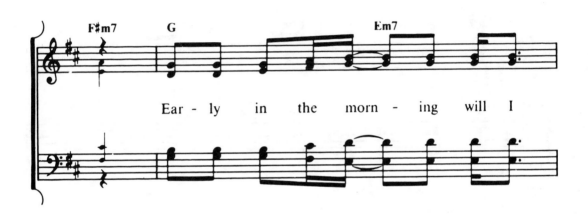

Ear - ly in the morn - ing will I

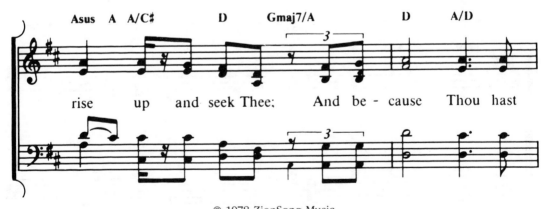

rise up and seek Thee; And be - cause Thou hast

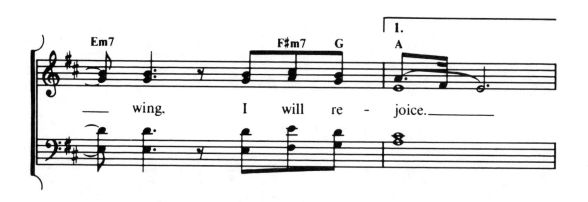

Medley options: Lord, I'm Gonna Love You; Like a Shepherd.

There is therefore now no condemnation
for those who are in Christ Jesus. Romans 8:1

No Condemnation   130

Words and Music by
CHARLES F. MONROE

Medley options: In Your Presence; Such Joy.

And there is salvation in no one else; for there is no other name under heaven that has been given among men, by which we must be saved. Acts 4:12

No Other Name

Words and Music by
ROBERT GAY

No oth-er name but the name of Je-sus, no oth-er name but the name of the Lord; No oth-er name but the name of Je-sus is wor-thy of glo-ry, and wor-thy of hon-or, and wor-thy of pow-er and all praise. No oth-er praise. His

Medley options: I Extol You; Highest Place.

132

No weapon that is formed against you shall prosper; and every tongue that accuses you in judgement you will condemn. Isaiah 54:17

No Weapon Formed

Author Unknown

No wea-pon formed against me shall pros-per,
all those who rise up a-gainst me shall fall;
I will not fear what the Dev-il may bring me, I am a ser-vant of God,
Oh, I am a ser-vant of God.

Medley options: The Lord Is Come; Blessed Be the Rock.

"Not by might nor by power, but by my Spirit," says the Lord of hosts. Zechariah 4:6

Not by Might nor Power   133

Words and Music by
MARK CAULK

Medley options: The Mighty One of Israel.

134   O, Clap Your Hands

Words and Music by
BILLY FUNK

In the cit-y of___ our God,_____ in the moun-tain of His ho - li - ness._____

Medley options: From the Rising of the Sun; Blessed Be the Rock

Thy face, O Lord, I shall seek. Psalm 27:8

135 O Lord, You're Beautiful

Words and Music by
KEITH GREEN

Medley options: More Precious Than Silver; Only Jesus.

The message of the cross is foolishness to those who are perishing,
but to us who are being saved it is the power of God. 1 Corinthians 1:18

O, Mighty Cross

136

Words and Music by
DAVID BARONI and JOHN CHISUM

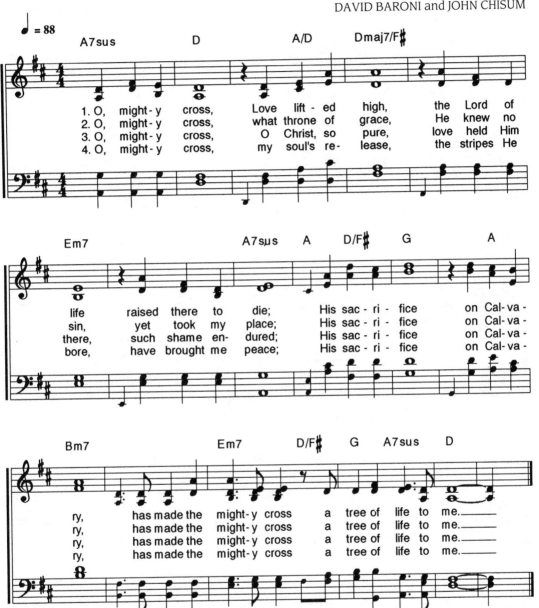

1. O, might-y cross, Love lift-ed high, the Lord of life raised there to die; His sac-ri-fice on Cal-va-ry, has made the might-y cross a tree of life to me.
2. O, might-y cross, what throne of grace, He knew no sin, yet took my place; His sac-ri-fice on Cal-va-ry, has made the might-y cross a tree of life to me.
3. O, might-y cross, O Christ, so pure, love held Him there, such shame en-dured; His sac-ri-fice on Cal-va-ry, has made the might-y cross a tree of life to me.
4. O, might-y cross, my soul's re-lease, the stripes He bore, have brought me peace; His sac-ri-fice on Cal-va-ry, has made the might-y cross a tree of life to me.

Medley options: I See the Lord; More of You.

137

Oh, the Glory
of Your Presence

Words and Music by
STEVEN L. FRY

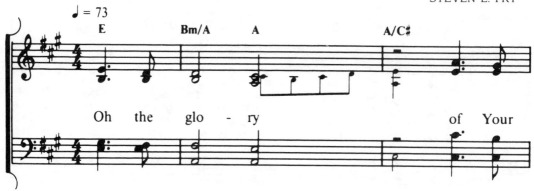

Oh the glo - ry   of Your

pres - ence._____ We Your tem - ple_____

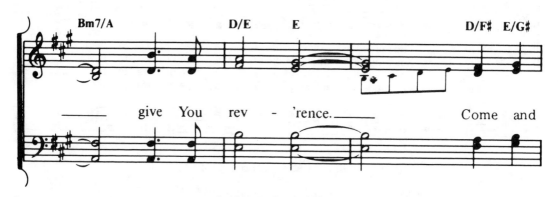

_____ give You rev - 'rence._____ Come and

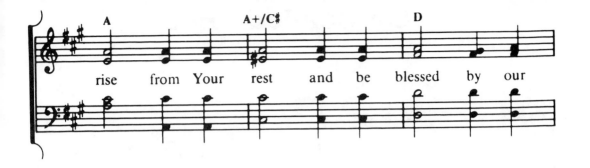

rise from Your rest and be blessed by our

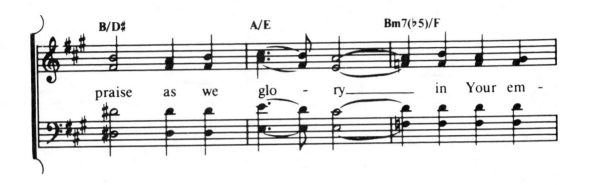

praise as we glo - ry_____ in Your em -

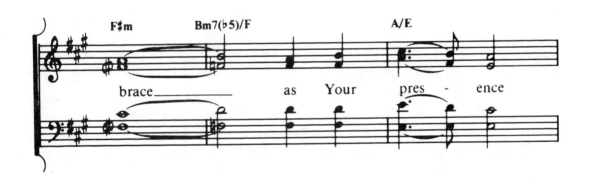

brace_____ as Your pres - ence

now fills this place._____

Medley options: I Will Magnify; Great Is the Lord.

*...that at the name of Jesus every knee should bow, of those who are
in heaven, and on earth, and under the earth. Philippians 2:10*

On Bended Knee

Words and Music by
ROBERT GAY

On__ bend-ed knee__ I come,__ with a
bend-ed knee__ we come,__ with a

hum-ble heart__ I come,__ bow-ing down be-fore__
hum-ble heart__ we come,__ bow-ing down be-fore__

__ Your ho-ly throne;__ Lift-ing ho-ly hands__ to You,-
__ Your ho-ly throne;__ Lift-ing ho-ly hands__ to You,-

__ as I pledge my love__ a-new,__ I wor-ship You__ in spir-
__ as we pledge our love__ a-new,__ we wor-ship You__ in spir-

Medley options: All Creation Worships You; All Hail King Jesus.

Hear, O Israel! The Lord is our God, the Lord is one! Deuteronomy 6:4

139 One God

Words and Music by
BOB FITTS

♩=138 **CHORUS**

Hear,— O Is-ra-el, the Lord, thy God— is one God, Hal-le-lu-

last time to CODA

jah! Hear,— O Is-ra-el, the Lord, thy God— is

VERSE

one God, Hal-le-lu-jah! And thou shalt love the Lord thy—

God with all thy— heart, with all thy might;—— And

give Him glo - ry,— King of glo - ry,— in His ways de -

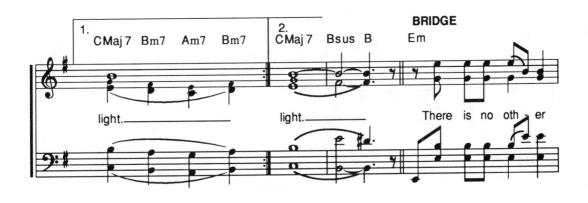

1. CMaj7 Bm7 Am7 Bm7 **2.** CMaj7 Bsus B **BRIDGE** Em

light._____ light._____ There is no oth - er

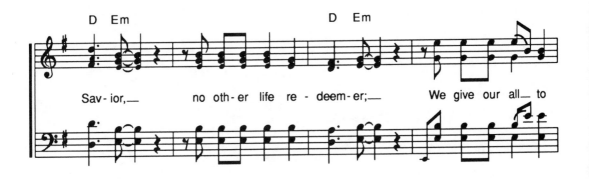

D Em D Em

Sav - ior,— no oth - er life re - deem - er;— We give our all— to

Medley options: The Lord Reigns.

Let us therefore draw near with confidence to the throne of grace. Hebrews 4:16

Only By Grace

140

Words and Music by
GERRIT GUSTAFSON

Medley options: Change My Heart, Oh God.

141

Salvation is found in no one else, for there is no other name under heaven given to men by which we must be saved. Acts 4:12

Only Jesus

Words and Music by
JOHN CHISUM

1. On - ly Je - sus_____ has the pow - er_____ of sal - va - tion_____ in His blood;_____ On - ly Je - sus_____ has the pow - er_____ of sal - va - tion_____ in His blood.

2. Hal - le - lu - jah, hal - le - lu - jah, our sal - va - tion is in His blood; Hal - le - lu - jah, hal - le - lu - jah, our sal - va - tion is in His blood.

Medley options: Crown Him; Salvation Belongs to Our God.

*With trumpets and the sound of the horn, shout
joyfully before the King, the Lord. Psalm 98:6*

Our God Is Lifted Up

Words and Music by
TIM SMITH

Medley options: Above All Else; We Declare That the Kingdom of God Is Here.

Our Heart

Words
JOHN CHISUM

CHORUS

Our__ heart,____ our de-sire,____ is to see the na-tions wor-ship,__ our__ cry,____ our__ prayer,____ is to sing Your praise to the ends of__ the earth; That with one might-y voice ev-'ry tribe and tongue re-joic-es,____ our__ heart,

rise   in   hon - est   wor - ship,   to   de -

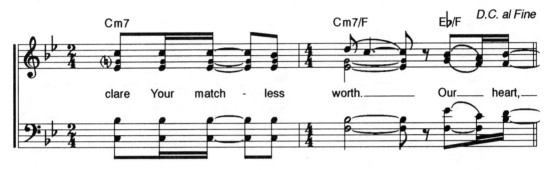

clare   Your   match - less   worth._____   Our____   heart,____

Medley options: Song for the Nations.

144 People of God

Words and Music by
WAYNE WATSON

1. With our lips let us sing one con - fes - sion, with our hearts hold to one truth a - lone;____ For__ He has e - rased our trans - gres - sion, claimed us and called us His own,____ His ver - y own.

2. Hear us, O spir - its of dark - ness, so you will know where we__ stand:____ We are His ser - vants__ pur - chased with scars, bought by the blood of the Lamb,__ the blood of the Lamb.____

CHORUS

We're the peo - ple of God, called by His

name, called from the dark and de-liv-ered from shame; One ho-ly

race— saints ev-'ry-one, be-cause of the blood of

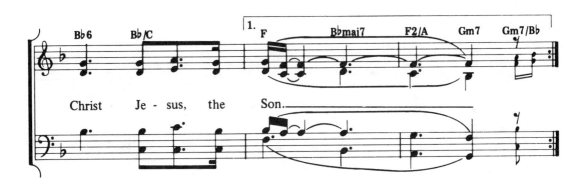

Christ Je-sus, the Son.

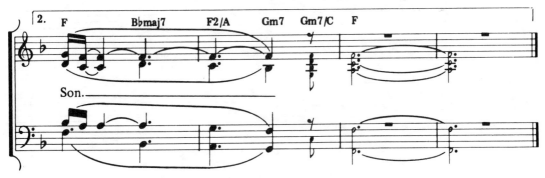

Son.

Medley options: I Will Bless Thee, O Lord.

145

With my mouth I will greatly extol the Lord; in the great throng I will praise Him. Psalm 109:30

Praise Him

Words and Music by
LYNN DeSHAZO

CHORUS

Praise Him, praise Him, praise Him, praise Him; Praise Him, praise Him, praise Him, praise Him. Fine

VERSE

1. We have as - sem - bled to
2. We are Your chil - dren, we've

D.C. al Fine

Dm7   Gsus   G

geth - er   now_____   and   sing._____
how   our   hearts_____   re - joice._____

Medley options: All Creation Worships You; To Him Who Sits on the Throne.

*O my Strength, I sing praise to You; You, O God,
are my fortress, my loving God. Psalm 59:17*

Praise to You

Words and Music by
LYNN DeSHAZO

Medley options: Give Thanks.

Blessed are the pure in heart, for they shall see God. Matthew 5:8

147 Pure in Heart

Words and Music by
DON HARRIS

Lord, make me pure in heart, make my heart faith-ful and true; So when You look at me it's Your right-eous-ness You see, Lord, make me pure in heart.

Medley options: Heaven Is in My Heart; Why So Downcast?

148

Teach me Your way, O Lord; I will walk in Thy truth,
unite my heart to fear Thy name. Psalm 86:11

Purify My Heart

Words and Music by
EUGENE GRECO

♩ = 104 **VERSE**

Teach me Your ways,___ O___ Lord,___ my___ God,___ and
I will___ walk in Your___ truth;
Give___ me a to - tal - ly___ un - di - vid - ed heart,___ that
I may fear Your___ name.___

CHORUS

Pu - ri - fy— my heart,— cleanse me, Lord,— I pray,—

re - move from me— all— that is

stand - ing in— the— way;—

Pu - ri - fy— my heart,— cleanse me, Lord,— I pray,—

re - move from me— all— that is

stand - ing in___ the___ way;_____ of Your love._____

Medley options: God Is the Strength of My Heart.

Awake, awake, put on strength, O arm of the Lord. Isaiah 51:9

Raise Up an Army 149

Words and Music by
STEVE and VIKKI COOK

Medley options: Our God Is Lifted Up; We Declare That the Kingdom of God Is Here.

The steps of a man are established by the Lord;
and He delights in his ways. Psalm 37:23

Rejoice, for the Steps

Words and Music by
HENRY GASKINS

Medley options: My Life Is in You, Lord; How Good It Is; Sing, Shout, Clap.

Rejoice in the Lord

151

Words and Music by
RUSSELL L. LOWE

Medley options: The Name of the Lord; Lift Up Your Countenance.

152

For the kingdom of God is...righteousness,
peace and joy in the Holy Spirit. Romans 14:17

Righteousness,
Peace and Joy

Words and Music by
HELENA BARRINGTON

With an "island" feel
♩ = 176 VERSE

Right - eous - ness,   peace,____   joy____ in the Ho - ly Ghost;____

Right - eous - ness, peace,___ and joy____ in the Ho - ly Ghost,

that's the King - dom of God.____   Right - eous - ness,   peace,____

joy____ in the Ho - ly Ghost;____

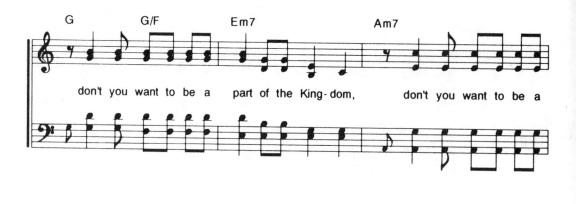

don't you want to be a part of the King-dom, don't you want to be a

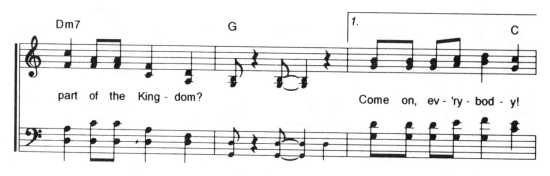

part of the King-dom? Come on, ev-'ry-bod-y!

Come on, ev-'ry-bod-y!

(repeat as desired)

1.4. There's____ love____ in the King-dom,
2.5. There's____ peace____ in the King-dom,
3.6. There's____ joy____ in the King-dom,
7. I'm an heir____ of the King-dom,

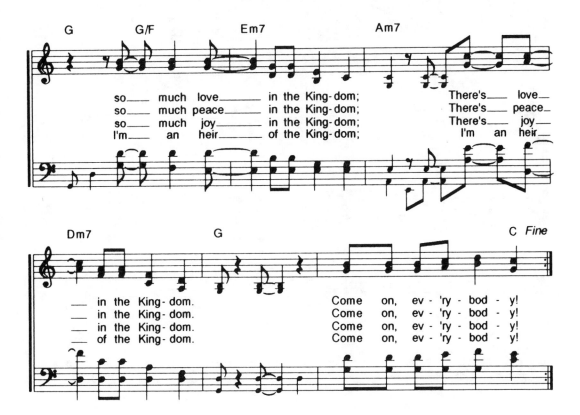

so___ much love___	in the King-dom;		There's___ love___
so___ much peace___	in the King-dom;		There's___ peace___
so___ much joy___	in the King-dom;		There's___ joy___
I'm___ an heir___	of the King-dom;		I'm an heir___

___ in the King-dom.	Come on, ev - 'ry - bod - y!
___ in the King-dom.	Come on, ev - 'ry - bod - y!
___ in the King-dom.	Come on, ev - 'ry - bod - y!
___ of the King-dom.	Come on, ev - 'ry - bod - y!

Medley options: Celebrate Jesus; No Condemnation.

*To Him who sits on the throne, and to the Lamb, be blessing
and honor and glory and dominion forever and ever. Revelation 5:13*

Salvation Belongs
to Our God

Words and Music by
ADRIAN HOWARD and PAT TURNER

1. Sal - va - tion be-longs__ to our God, Who sits up - on the throne,_____ and un - to__ the Lamb;_____ Praise and glo - ry,__ wis - dom and thanks, hon - or__ and pow - er__ and strength_____

2. And we the re-deemed__ shall be strong in pur - pose and un - i - ty, de - clar - ing__ a - loud;_____ Praise and glo - ry,__ wis - dom and thanks, hon - or__ and pow - er__ and strength_____

CHORUS

be to our God for - ev - er__ and ev - er;

Medley options: Great Is the Lord; Forever Grateful.

154 **Sanctuary**

Words and Music by
JOHN THOMPSON and RANDY SCRUGGS

Medley options: Instruments of Your Peace; More of You.

Christ will shine on you. Ephesians 5:14

Shine, Jesus, Shine

155

Words and Music by
GRAHAM KENDRICK

Medley options: Firm Foundation.

Sing to Him a new song; play skillfully with a shout of joy. Psalm 33:3

Sing, Shout, Clap

156

Words and Music by
BILLY FUNK

CHORUS
In a shuffle

Sing, shout, clap your hands, give praise un-to your Mak-er, make a joy-ful noise un-to the Lord; Sing, shout, clap your hands, give praise un-to your Mak-er, for the Lord, He is Al-might-y God.

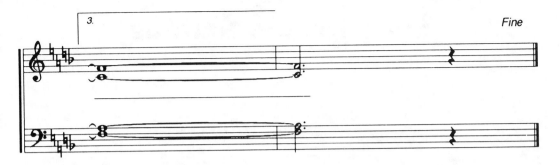

Medley options: My Life Is in You, Lord; How Good It Is; Rejoice, for the Steps.

"Go therefore and make disciples of all the nations,...teaching them to observe all that I commanded you; and lo, I am with you always, even to the end of the age." Matthew 28:19,20

157 Song for the Nations

Words and Music by
CHRIS CHRISTENSEN

1. May we be a shin - ing light to the na - tions,
(2. May we bring a) word of hope to the na - tions,
(3. May we be a) heal - ing balm to the na - tions,
(4. May we sing a) song of joy to the na - tions,
(5. May Your) king - dom come to the na - tions,

a shin - ing light to the peo - ples of the earth; Til the
a word of life to the peo - ples of the earth; Til the
a heal - ing balm to the peo - ples of the earth; Til the
a song of praise to the peo - ples of the earth; Til the
Your will be done in the peo - ples of the earth; Til the

whole world sees the___ glo - ry of Your name.
whole world knows there's sal - va - tion through Your name.
whole world knows the___ pow - er of Your name.
whole world rings with the prais es of Your name.
whole world knows that___ Je - sus Christ is Lord.

Medley options: Blessed Be the Lord God Almighty; Our Heart.

158 Spirit of the Living God

Words and Music by
PETE SANCHEZ, JR.

Medley options: I Exalt Thee; Exalt the Lord Our God.

159 # Such Joy

Words and Music by
DON HARRIS

Lyrics:

CHORUS
Such joy! Such un-speak-a-ble joy, such peace, an ev-er-last-ing peace; Such love, a pure and ho-ly love, Spir-it, have Your way in me.

There's a

VERSE
peace that floods my soul when the Spir-it of the Lord

Medley options: In Your Presence; Lift Him Up; Why So Downcast?

We have confidence to enter the holy place by the blood of Jesus. Hebrews 10:19

160 Take Me In

Words and Music by
DAVE BROWNING

♩ = 58
VERSE

Take me past the out - er courts,_ and thru the ho - ly place,_ past the bra-zen al - tar; Lord, I wan-na see Your face._ Pass me by the crowds of peo - ple, the priests who sing their praise;_ I hun-ger and thirst for Your right-eous-ness and it's on-ly found one place._ So take me in_

Medley options: More Love, More Power.

161

Thanks Be to God

**Words and Music by
Tim Picking**

Thanks be— to God,— Who leads us in— His tri - umph.—

Thanks be— to God,— Who's got the vic - to-ry.—

Thanks be— to God,— Who leads us in— His tri - umph.—

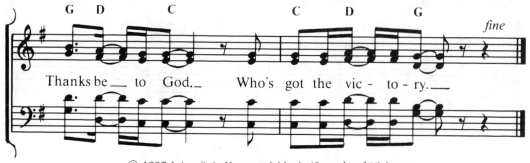

Thanks be— to God,— Who's got the vic - to-ry.—

VERSE

We have ov - er - come the world by the blood of the Lamb
Through the blood of our Sav-ior, we are set free from the curse.

and lov-ing not our lives ev - en un - to death.
Je-sus is the one and on-ly last-ing sac - ri - fice.

The word of our tes - ti - mo-ny tells the world a-bout His love, as we shout un -
He has con-quered Sa-tan's po-wer. No-more shall we be a-shamed. Just as He de -

D.C. al Fine

to the na-tions He is com-ing back! Oh He is com-ing back!
feat-ed death. we shall nev-er die. no we shall nev-er die.

Medley options: Lift Him Up; Why So Downcast?

Do not fear or be dismayed...for the battle is not yours but God's. II Chronicles 20:15

162 The Battle Belongs to the Lord

Words and Music by
JAMIE OWENS-COLLINS

CHORUS

Medley options: One God.

163

The Lord builds up Jerusalem; He gathers the outcasts of Israel.
He heals the brokenhearted, and binds up their wounds. Psalm 147:2,3

The Lord Is
Building Jerusalem

Words and Music by
RICH COOK

The Lord is build-ing Jeru - sa - lem, the
Lord is build-ing Jeru - sa-lem, gath-er-ing to-geth-er the
out-casts of Is-ra-el, heal-ing bro-ken hearts, bind-ing up their wounds.
The Lord is build-ing, the Lord is build-ing up Je-ru - sa - lem.

Medley options: Make a Joyful Noise; Blow the Trumpet in Zion.

And a Redeemer will come to Zion. Isaiah 59:20

The Lord Is Come

164

Words and Music by
RIC MARCHI

The Lord is come in glo-ry and pow-er, the
Lord is come, sing praise to His name; The Lord is come Ho-san
na, Ho-san-na, the Lord is come, sing praise to His name. The
to His name. For the Lord is come to Zi-on, He will

Medley options: Come and Worship; No Weapon Formed.

The Lord Reigns

165

Words and Music by
DAN STRADWICK

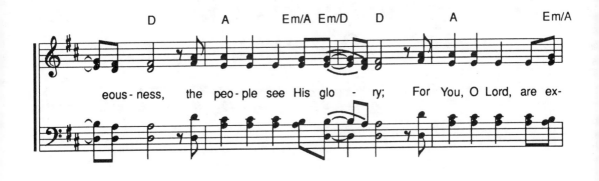

eous-ness, the peo-ple see His glo - ry; For You, O Lord, are ex-

alt-ed o-ver all__ the earth,__ o-ver all__ the earth._____ The

reigns.__ Our God reigns,__ our God reigns!__

Medley options: One God.

166 The Mighty One of Israel

Words and Music by
JIM and GINGER HENDRICKS

♩ = 120

1. The Lord shall cause His glo - ri - ous voice___ to be heard, and
2. The eyes___ of the blind shall be o - pened and they'll see, the
3. The Lord shall cause His glo - ri - ous beau - ty to be seen, the

you shall have a song___ in the night;
ears___ of the deaf___ shall___ hear; The
des - ert shall bloom___ and re - joice;

Come to the moun - tain___ of___ the Lord,
lame man shall jump and___ shall leap as a hart, the
Say to___ them that___ are fear - ful of heart, be

see His glo - ry and___ His___ might. He's the
tongue___ of the dumb___ shall___ sing. He's the
strong___ and lis - ten to His voice. He's the

Medley options: Not by Might nor Power.

167

Thou hast been a refuge for me, a tower of
strength against the enemy. Psalm 61:3

The Name of the Lord

Words and Music by
CURTIS PEIFER

O the name of the Lord,___ it's like a strong tow - er; The
right - eous___ shall run un - to it and be glad. O the
name of the Lord,___ it's like a strong tow - er; The
right - eous___ shall run un - to it. O the

Medley options: Rejoice in the Lord; Lift Up Your Countenance.

Who is this King of glory? The Lord strong and mighty,
the Lord mighty in battle. Psalm 24:8

The Spirit of the Lord

Words and Music by
BILLY FUNK

Medley options: Clap, Clap Your Hands.

The Lord's lovingkindnesses indeed never cease, for his compassions never fail.
They are new every morning; great is Thy faithfulness. Lamentations 3:22,23

The Steadfast Love of the Lord

Words and Music by
EDITH McNEILL

Medley options: Think About His Love; Extol the Name.

There Is None Holy as the Lord

Words and Music by
GARY GARRETT

Medley options: Great Is the Lord; Oh, the Glory of Your Presence.

171 There Is None Like You

O Lord, there is none like Thee, neither is there
any God besides Thee. 1 Chronicles 17:20

Words and Music by
LENNY LeBLANC

CHORUS

There is none like You, no one else can touch my heart like You do; I could search for all e-ter-ni-ty long and find there is none like You.

Medley options: Joy of My Desire; Lord, I'm Gonna Love You.

But God, being rich in mercy, because of His great love with which He loved us, even when we were dead in our transgressions, made us alive together with Christ. Ephesians 2:4,5

Think About His Love

Words and Music by
WALT HARRAH

Think a-bout His love._____ think a-bout His good-ness._____ think a-bout His grace that's brought us through._____ For as high as the hea-vens a-bove_____ so

Medley options: Highest Place; More Than Anything.

This is the day which the Lord has made; let us rejoice and be glad in it. Psalm 118:24

This Is the Day

173

Words and Music by
RICK SHELTON

VERSE 2

Lord. Cel-e-brate the pres-ence of the Lord, for He is wor-thy to be praised; Cel-e-brate the pres-ence of the Lord, for He is wor-thy to be praised. Re-

Lord. Re-joice!

Fine

Medley options: Celebrate Jesus; Come and Worship.

Worthy art Thou, our Lord and our God, to receive glory and honor and power; for Thou didst create all things, and because of Thy will they existed, and were created. Revelation 4:11

174

Thou Art Worthy

Words and Music by
PAULINE M. MILLS

♩ = 77

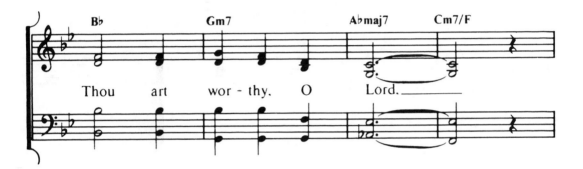

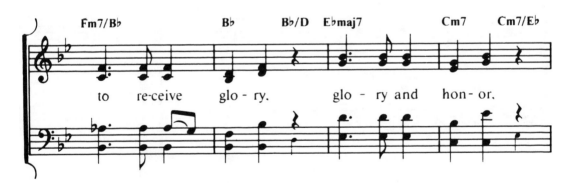

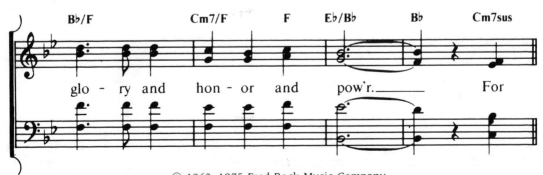

Medley options: In Moments Like These; Worthy the Lamb That Was Slain.

Thou Art Worthy, Great Jehovah

175

Words and Music by
KAREN EAGAN

Thou art wor - thy._____ Great Je -

ho - vah._____ Thou art wor - thy._____

____ Might - y God._____ Thou art

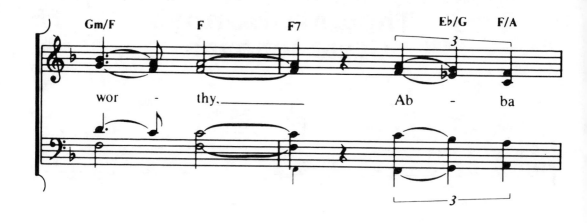

Medley options: More Precious Than Silver; Exalt the Lord Our God.

To Him Who Sits
on the Throne

176

Words and Music by
DEBBYE GRAAFSMA

To Him who sits on the throne_____

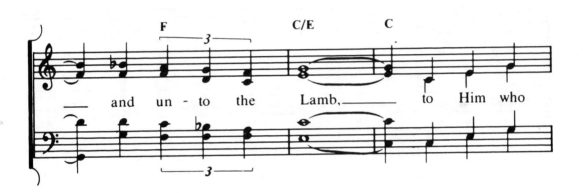

_____ and un - to the Lamb,_____ to Him who

sits on the throne_____ and un - to the

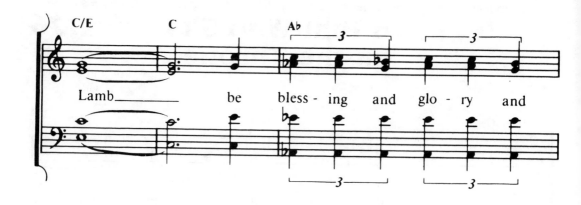

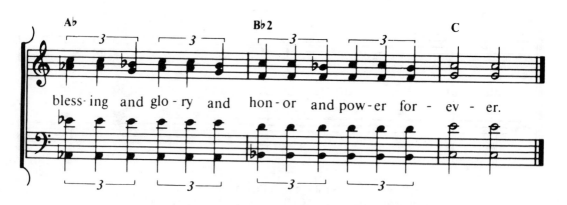

Medley options: You Are My God; I See the Lord.

To Thee
We Ascribe Glory

177

Words and Music by
KIRK DEARMAN

Medley options: Hosanna; I Worship You, Almighty God.

For you will go out with joy and be led forth with peace. Isaiah 55:12

178   Trees of the Field

Words and Music by
STUART DAUERMANN and STEFFI GEISER RUBIN

You shall go out with joy_ and be led forth with peace._

The moun-tains and the hills will break forth be-fore you; There'll be

shouts of joy,_ and all the trees of the field will

clap, will clap their hands. And all the

CHORUS

trees of the field will clap their hands.___ the

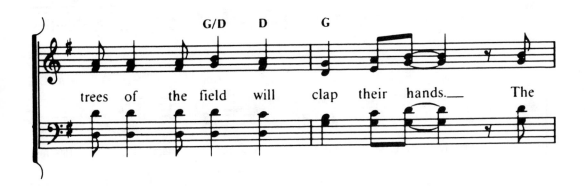

trees of the field will clap their hands.___ The

trees of the field will clap their hands___ and

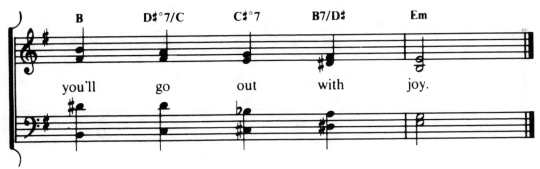

you'll go out with joy.

Medley options: Jehovah Jireh; Go Forth.

179

The king's heart is in the hand of the Lord, like the rivers of water;
He turns it wherever He wishes. Proverbs 21:1

Turn My Heart

Words and Music by
LYNN DeSHAZO

Turn my heart, O Lord, like riv-ers___ of wa - ter,___
— turn my heart, O Lord,___ by Your___ hand;___ Till my
whole life flows___ in the riv - er of Your Spir - it,___
and my___ name___ brings hon - or___ to the

Medley options: We Are an Offering; My Soul Follows Hard After Thee.

180

Under the Blood

Words and Music by
MARTIN J. NYSTROM and RHONDA GUNTER SCELSI

VERSE

O the blood of the Pass-o-ver Lamb is ap-plied to the door___ of my life,___ no pow-er of dark-ness could ev-er with-stand the force of the blood___ sac-ri-fice;___ Though

Medley options: He Is Exalted; We Bow Down.

...the battle is not yours but God's. 2 Chronicles 20:15

Victory Song (Through Our God)

181

Words and Music by
DALE GARRATT

VERSE

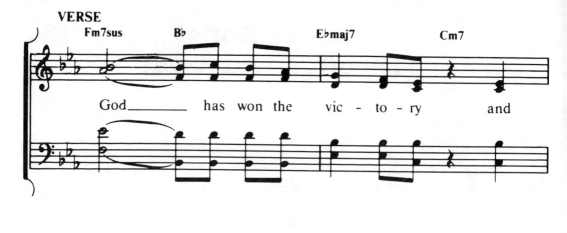

God_____ has won the vic - to - ry and

set_____ His peo - ple free. His

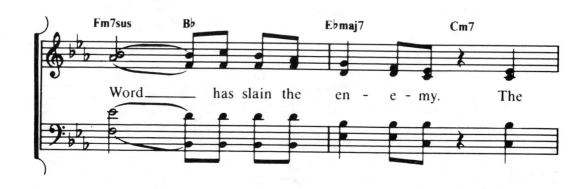

Word_____ has slain the en - e - my. The

D.S. al fine

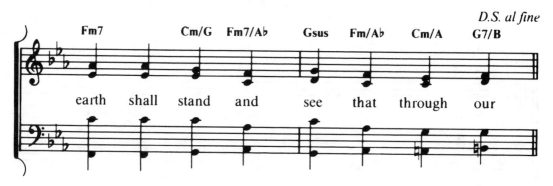

earth shall stand and see that through our

Medley options: For the Lord Is Marching On.

182

Present your bodies a living and holy sacrifice, acceptable to God,
which is your spiritual service of worship. Romans 12:1

We Are an Offering

Words and Music by
DWIGHT LILES

We lift our voi - ces,— we lift our hands,— we lift our lives— up to You, we are an of-fer-ing;— Lord, use our voi - ces,— Lord, use our hands,— Lord, use our lives,— they are Yours, we are an of-fer-ing.——

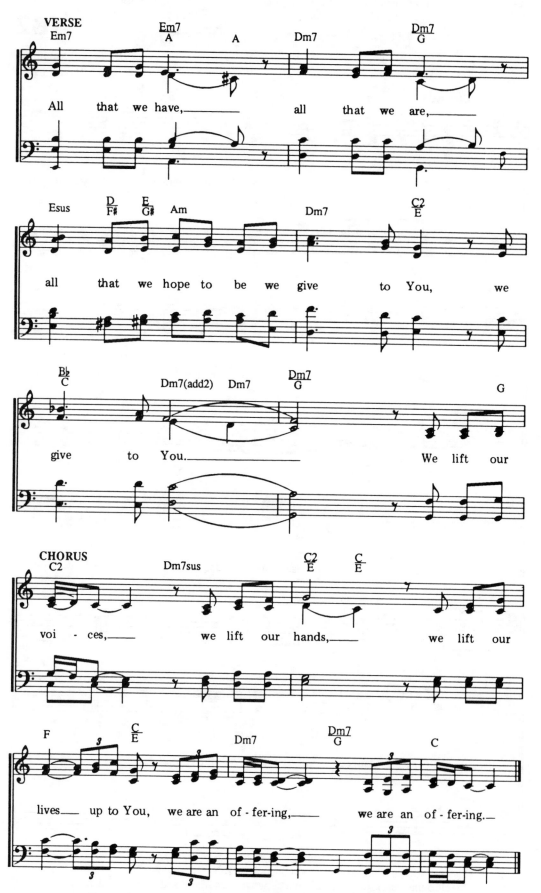

Medley options: Anointing, Fall on Me; Lord, I'm Gonna Love You.

I bow my knees before the Father. Ephesians 3:14

We Bow Down

183

Words and Music by
TWILA PARIS

1. You are Lord of cre-a-tion and Lord of my life,
(2. You are) King of cre-a-tion and King of my life,

Lord of the land and the sea; You were
King of the land and the sea; You were

Lord of the heav-ens be-fore there was time, And
King of the heav-ens be-fore there was time, And

Lord of all lords You will be. We bow
King of all kings You will be. We bow

Medley options: Under the Blood; He Is Exalted.

We Bring the Sacrifice of Praise

184

Words and Music by
KIRK DEARMAN

CHORUS

of - fer up to You____ the sac - ri -

fi - ces of thanks - giv - ing and we

of - fer up to You____ the sac - ri -

fi - ces of joy.

Medley options: In Him We Live; Ah, Lord God; What a Mighty God We Serve.

185

And whatsoever city you enter, and they receive you . . . heal those in it who are sick,
and say to them, "The kingdom of God has come near to you." Luke 10:8,9

We Declare That the Kingdom of God Is Here

Words and Music by
GRAHAM KENDRICK

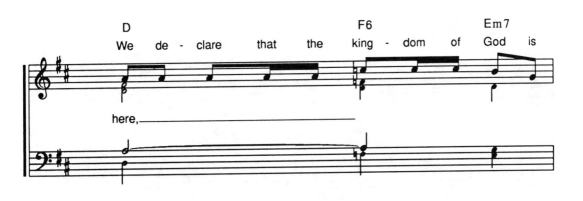

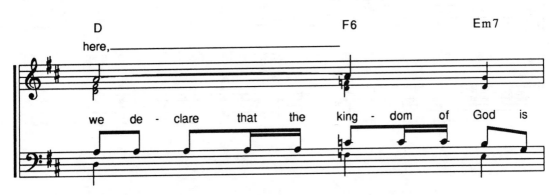

Medley options: Above All Else; Raise Up an Army.

186

And they overcame him because of the blood of the Lamb and because of the word of their testimony. Revelation 12:11

We Have Overcome

Words and Music by
DANIEL GARDNER

♩ = 128

We have o-ver-come___ by the blood of the Lamb,_____ by the

pow-er of___ His blood___ we___ will stand;

We have o-ver-come___ by the blood of the Lamb,___ and

He will bring the vic - to - ry._____

Medley options: More Than Conquerors.

I will...glorify Thy name forever. Psalm 86:12

We Will Glorify

187

Words and Music by
TWILA PARIS

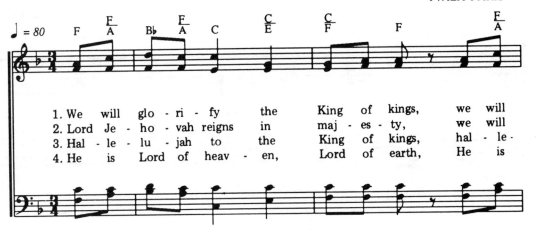

1. We will glo - ri - fy the King of kings, we will
2. Lord Je - ho - vah reigns in maj - es - ty, we will
3. Hal - le - lu - jah to the King of kings, hal - le -
4. He is Lord of heav - en, Lord of earth, He is

glo - ri - fy the___ Lamb; We will glo - ri - fy the
bow be - fore His___ throne; We will wor - ship Him in
lu - jah to the___ Lamb; Hal - le - lu - jah to the
Lord of all who___ live; He is Lord a - bove the

Lord of lords, for He is the great I___ Am.
right - eous-ness, we will wor-ship Him a - lone.
Lord of lords, for He is the great I___ Am.
u - ni - verse, all___ praise to Him we___ give.

Medley·options: Crown Him; All Hail King Jesus.

His name shall be called . . . Mighty God. Isaiah 9:6

188 What a Mighty God
We Serve

Author Unknown

What a might - y God we serve,____

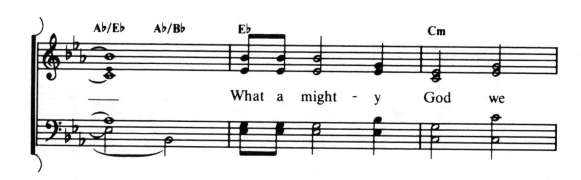

____ What a might - y God we

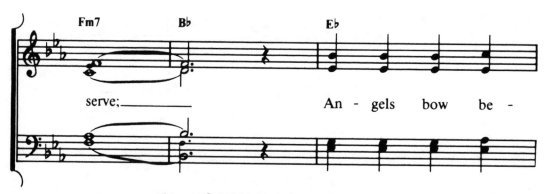

serve;_____ An - gels bow be -

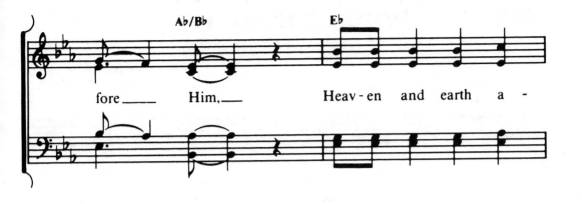

fore____ Him,___ Heav-en and earth a -

dore___ Him,___ What a might - y

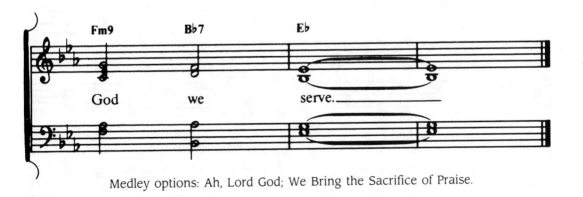

God we serve._____

Medley options: Ah, Lord God; We Bring the Sacrifice of Praise.

189 When I Look Into Your Holiness

Words and Music by
WAYNE and CATHY PERRIN

VERSE

When I look in-to Your ho-li-ness,— when I
found the joy of reach-ing Your heart,— when my

gaze in-to Your love-li-ness, When all
will be-comes en-thralled in— Your love,

1.
things that sur-round be-come shad-ows in the light of You.

2.
When I've You.— I wor-ship

Medley options: I Worship You, Almighty God; I Am the God That Healeth Thee.

Who is like Thee among the gods, O Lord? Exodus 15:11

190 Who Is Like Unto Thee

Words and Music by
JUDY HORNER MONTEMAYOR

Medley options: Amazing Love; You Are My God.

Why So Downcast? **191**

Words and Music by
FRANK BERRIOS, TOM BROOKS and JEFF HAMLIN

soul._____
Bless the Lord,— my soul.

soul._____
Bless the Lord,— my soul.

Bless the Lord,—

BRIDGE

He's the lift - er of___ my coun - te-nance, bless the Lord,—

He's the lift - er of___ my head; Bless the Lord,—

He's the lift - er of___ my coun - te-nance;

I will nev - er be___ a - shamed._____ Oh,_____

Medley options: I Will Call Upon the Lord; Clap Your Hands.

Worthy is the Lamb that was slain. Revelation 5:12

Worthy the Lamb That Was Slain

192

Words and Music by
DON MOEN

Medley options: Thou Art Worthy; I Will Bless the Lord.

193 Worthy, You Are Worthy

Words and Music by
DON MOEN

1. Wor - thy, You are wor - thy,
2. Ho - ly, You are ho - ly, King of
3. Je - sus, You are Je - sus.

kings, Lord of lords, You are wor - thy;
You are ho - ly;
You are Je - sus;

Wor - thy, You are wor - thy,
Ho - ly, You are ho - ly, King of
Je - sus, You are Je - sus.

kings, Lord of lords, I wor - ship You.

Medley options: Blessed Be the Name of the Lord; I Am the God That Healeth Thee.

His eyes are a flame of fire and on His head are many diadems. Revelation 19:12

194

You Are Crowned With Many Crowns

Words and Music by
JOHN SELLERS

Medley options: The Lord Reigns; I Love to Praise Him.

195

And every tongue confess that Jesus Christ is Lord,
to the glory of God the Father. Philippians 2:11

You Are Lord
of Everything

Words and Music by
PAUL BALOCHE

Medley options: I See the Lord; Highest Place.

O God, Thou art my God. Psalm 63:1

You Are My God

196

Words and Music by
MACON DELAVAN

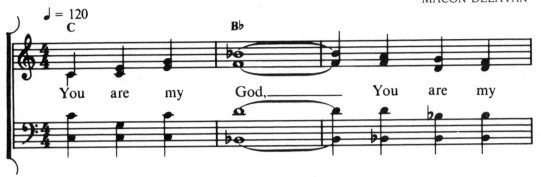

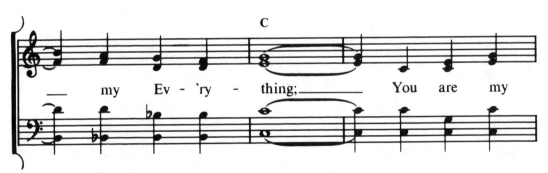

Lord,_____ that's why I sing to

You. "Hal - le - lu - jah,_____

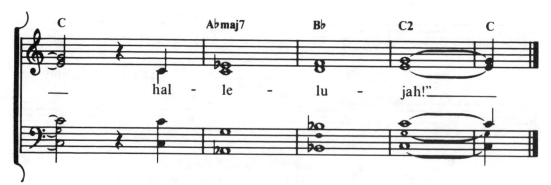

____ hal - le - lu - jah!"_____

Medley options: To Him Who Sits on the Throne; Thou Art Worthy, Great Jehovah.

Therefore also God highly exalted Him, and bestowed on Him the name which is above every name. Philippians 2:9

You Have Been Given 197

Words and Music by
BOB KAUFLIN

1. You have been giv-en the name a-bove all names, and we wor-ship You, yes, we wor-ship You; You have been giv-en the name a-bove all names, and we wor-ship You, and we wor-ship
2. We are Your peo-ple made for Your glo-ry, and we wor-ship You, yes, we wor-ship You; We are Your peo-ple made for Your glo-ry, and we wor-ship You, and we wor-ship
3. You have re-deemed us from ev-'ry na-tion, and we wor-ship You, yes, we wor-ship You; You have re-deemed us from ev-'ry na-tion, and we wor-ship You, and we wor-ship

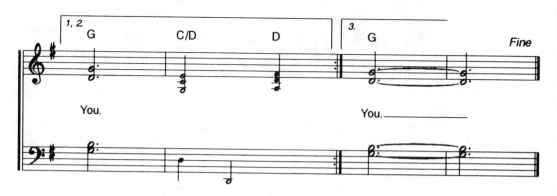

Medley options: I Sing Praises; We Will Glorify.

I will sing to the Lord, because He has dealt bountifully with me. Psalm 13:6

You Have Been Good   198

Words and Music by
TWILA PARIS

Medley options: I Will Bless Thee, O Lord; Jesus, Name Above All Names.

...who has called you out of darkness into His marvelous light. 1 Peter 2:9

199 You Have Called Us

Words and Music by
LYNN DeSHAZO and MARTIN J. NYSTROM

You have called_____ us out of dark - ness, out of dark - ness in - to Your mar - vel - ous light; You have saved____ us from the dark - ness, we re - joice in Your pow - er and might.____ You have called____

Medley options: You Are Crowned with Many Crowns.

200 Your Steadfast Love

Words and Music by
TED SANDQUIST

Your stead - fast__ love ex - tends to the heav - ens,_____

__ Your faith - ful - ness reach - es to the clouds;_____

__ Your right - eous - ness__ is like maj - es - tic moun - tains,____

__ and Your wis - dom like the depths__ of__ the sea,

And You come____ to me,_____ fill - ing my

Medley options: He Who Began a Good Work in You.

Song Index A

Titles are in CAPITALS
First lines are in lower case type

Scripture Reference Index B

Topical Index C

COMMITMENT

CONSECRATION

DECLARATION

PRAISE

TESTIMONY

Key and Tempo Index D

A MAJOR
Fast
Moderate
Slow

A♭ MAJOR
Moderate

B♭ MAJOR
Fast
Moderate

D MAJOR, Fast, Cont'd.

D MINOR
Fast

E MAJOR
Fast

Moderate

E MINOR
Fast

F MAJOR, Moderate, Cont'd.

F MINOR
Fast

G MAJOR
Fast

Moderate

Slow

G MINOR

Moderate

Slow

Ready-to-Use Music Package Index E

Each songlist provides page numbers and key suggestions. You can extend or shorten the length of these music packages with very minor changes. We trust that you will find these lists useful and beneficial.

TITLE	SONG #	KEY
Worship Service #1		
Let The Redeemed	104	C, D^b
Ah, Lord God	3	D
What A Mighty God We Serve	188	E^b, E, F
All We Like Sheep	7	B^b
Thou Art Worthy	174	B^b
Holy Ground	65	E^b
Give Thanks	46	F
Worship Service #2		
No Condemnation	130	F
Your Steadfast Love	200	F
I Will Bless The Lord	84	F, G^b, G
I Will Magnify	88	G (F/G Transition)
All Creation Worships	5	C
Worship Service #3		
Blessed Be The Lord God Almighty	22	C
When I Look Into Your Holiness	189	C
Think About His Love	172	D
Lamb of God	100	E^b
More Precious Than Silver	122	F
The Steadfast Love of The Lord	169	G
Worship Service #4		
Let There Be Glory and Honor and Praises	105	G, A^b
Worthy, The Lamb That Was Slain	192	A
Shine, Jesus, Shine	155	A, B^b
Song For The Nations	157	B^b
Our Heart	143	B^b
Worship Service #5		
You Are Crowned With Many Crowns	194	G
My Life Is In You, Lord	128	G
I Will Call Upon The Lord	86	C
I Will Bless Thee, O Lord	85	D, E^b
Jesus, Name Above All Names	98	F
I Exalt Thee	38	F

Worship Service #6

He Who Began A Good Work	60	G
God Will Make A Way	52	G, A^b
God Is The Strength of my Heart	51	A^b
I Sing Praises	78	A
I Extol You	74	A
Be Exalted, O God	18	B^b

Worship Service #7

All Hail King Jesus	6	F
Lift High The Lord Our Banner	108	F
Lift Him Up	109	F, G^b
Almighty	8	G
To Him Who Sits On The Throne	176	C

Worship Service #8

Mighty Is Our God	118	B^b
Great And Mighty Is He	54	C
Great and Mighty Army	53	D
What A Mighty God We Serve	188	E^b, F
Mighty Warrior	119	F
More Than Conquerors	124	F

Worship Service #9

Let Your Spirit Rise Within Me	106	F, G^b
He Is The King of Kings	59	G
Heaven Is In My Heart	62	G
I Will Call Upon The Lord	86	C
You Are My God	196	C, D^b
Glory to the Lamb	48	D

Worship Service #10

In Him We Live	91	D
We Bring The Sacrifice of Praise	184	D, E^b
How Excellent Is Thy Name	67	E^b, F
He Is Exalted	57	F
We Will Glorify	187	F, G^b, G
I Worship You, Almighty God	90	G

Worship Service #11

Crown Him	37	A^b, A
Come Into His Presence (slow)	33	B^b
Come Into The King's Chambers	35	B^b
I Am The God That Healeth Thee	70	F
Here We Are	63	G, A^b
Oh The Glory Of Your Presence	137	A

Worship Service #12

Righteousness, Peace and Joy	152	C
Our God Is Lifted Up	142	D, E^b
Sing, Shout, Clap	156	F
Let Everything That Has Breath	101	G
Praise Him	145	C
We Are An Offering	182	C

Worship Service #13

Firm Foundation	42	F, G^b
Mourning Into Dancing	125	G
Be Magnified	20	G, A^b
There Is None Like You	171	A^b
There Is None Holy As The Lord	170	B^b

Worship Service #14

How Good It Is	68	F
Blessed Be The Name of The Lord	23	F, G^b
The Name of the Lord	167	G
Lift Up Your Countenance	110	A
Great Is The Lord	55	A
Anointing Fall On Me	12	D
Hear My Cry	61	D

Worship Service #15

My Help Comes From The Lord	127	E^b
Come and Worship	32	F, G^b
I Was Made To Praise You	82	G
I Want To Be Where You Are	81	G
Come Into The Holy of Holies	34	A^b